Hurd
430 Asland Ave
Cuy. Falls

PLANETS, STARS
AND SPACE

CREATIVE SCIENCE SERIES

ETTA SCHNEIDER RESS, Ed.D., *editor-in-chief*
GERHARD RAMBERG, *art editor*

PLANETS, STARS AND SPACE

Joseph Miles Chamberlain, Chairman
Thomas D. Nicholson, Associate Astronomer
American Museum-Hayden Planetarium

THE EARTH'S STORY

Gerald Ames and Rose Wyler
Authors, *The Golden Book of Astronomy, Restless Earth, The Story of the Ice Age*

THE WAY OF THE WEATHER

Jerome Spar, Ph.D., Associate Professor
Department of Meteorology and Oceanography
New York University, N. Y.

ATOMS, ENERGY AND MACHINES

Jack McCormick, Ph.D.
The American Museum of Natural History, New York, N. Y.

PLANETS, STARS AND SPACE

by

Joseph Miles Chamberlain, Chairman
Thomas D. Nicholson, Associate Astronomer

The American Museum-Hayden Planetarium
New York

In Co-operation with

THE AMERICAN MUSEUM OF NATURAL HISTORY

NEW YORK

Published by Creative Educational Society

1961
Printing

Illustrated by
Helmut Wimmer, American Museum-Hayden Planetarium, New York, N. Y.

Foreword

ASTRONOMY, we believe, is a fascinating subject. It is true that the objects concerned with the science are pretty well beyond our immediate reach. Yet we want to know as much about them as possible—if we care to be educated persons. The astronomical universe is an amazing thing. The other planets differ from the earth in various ways. Many stars are unlike our own star, the sun. The Milky Way, too, is a remarkable system, a vast conglomeration of stars, double stars, star clouds, star clusters, nebulae, and other objects. And beyond the Milky Way, at truly inconceivable distances, are millions upon millions of other galaxies, and these exist in all degrees of evolution.

Having had teaching experience in astronomy from grade school to college, the authors of this book have written in a concise, descriptive vein, without recourse to mathematics. They have used care in the choice of words, avoiding certain commonly used terms that are apt to carry the wrong connotations. Words like orbit, diameter, and eccentricity do not have proper substitutes, but possess a definite meaning.

Unlike a number of "first" books for the beginner in astronomy, this work provides rather an overall perspective on celestial objects, from the earth to the outer galaxies. Special care is used in the illustrations, including the diagrams and the pictures.

HUGH S. RICE, PH.D.
American Museum-Hayden Planetarium
New York

5

Contents

Contents *(continued)*

Introduction

PERHAPS one of the most common experiences men share is a curiosity about the skies. There is a natural wonder about the kind of universe represented by the things we see above us, and the place of the earth among them. The most practical value in astronomy lies in extending man's curiosity about the celestial environment into an organized accumulation of knowledge.

In our book, we have presented descriptive astronomy at its broadest, beginning with the earth and going outward in distance to define the structure and population of the universe. We have kept away from mathematics and technical language where possible, explaining them where they had to be used.

We have taken liberal advantage of one wonderful feature of modern astronomy—the photograph. It is no longer necessary to spend hours at an expensive telescope to see and enjoy the objects of astronomical study. These things are shown far better in the many excellent pictures available to us from the great observatories of the world. In them we can share the finest hours of the great astronomers, and the superlative vision of the best telescopes. It is through these pictures and the original art prepared for our book that the words of the text take on special meaning.

JOSEPH MILES CHAMBERLAIN
THOMAS D. NICHOLSON

CHAPTER 1

THE EARTH

NOTHING in the universe seems so familiar to us as the earth—the planet on which we live. Yet in many ways the earth is not well known. It has often been said that the cartographer could in some respects prepare a better map of the moon than of the earth. There are many parts of our world that have not been explored as well as the moon's surface has been explored by telescope.

It is useful to science to consider the earth as an object in space. Investigations of its surface, interior, atmosphere, and oceans cannot successfully be limited to small areas. They pose problems that are essentially universal, that require understanding of world-wide conditions before truly valuable solutions can be sought. This was one of the important goals of the vast scientific program known as the International Geophysical Year, conducted from July 1957 to December 1958. Science, during that study, looked upon the earth as a planet, as a world in space whose features could best be understood by considering it as a whole.

THE EARTH IS A PLANET

AMONG THE ASTRONOMERS of ancient Greece, two theories developed concerning the nature of the earth and its place in creation. One was heliocentric (sun-centered)—everything in the universe, including the earth, was supposed to revolve around the sun. The other was geocentric (earth-centered)—everything circled around the earth. The earth-centered idea gained prominence, spread throughout Europe, and was accepted for almost two thousand years. Until only a few centuries ago, astronomers, other learned men, and everyone else considered it the basic plan of the universe.

Claudius Ptolemy, an astronomer and philosopher of the first century A.D., left a good description of the geocentric theory. According to his description, the entire sky turned around the earth once each day in a westward direction, causing day and night and making the sun, moon, and stars rise and set. But the sun and moon, and five wandering stars moved slowly eastward around the earth, causing them to change their positions with respect to the background of stars as they rose and set each day. These objects were called planets, from the Greek word "planetes" which means "wandering star."

The geocentric idea was abandoned in the sixteenth and seventeenth centuries, partly as a result of the writings of Nikolaus Copernicus and partly because of observations made by the great astronomers Tycho Brahe, Johannus Kepler, and Galileo Galilei. It was shown that the wandering stars (planets) were revolving around the sun. Later observations proved conclusively that the earth also moved around the sun. It became obvious that the wandering stars and the earth were part of a solar system controlled by the sun.

Today, the word planet has a different meaning. Planets are large, round, mostly solid objects that revolve around the sun. There are nine objects in space that fit such a description. One of them is the earth. Therefore, the earth is a planet.

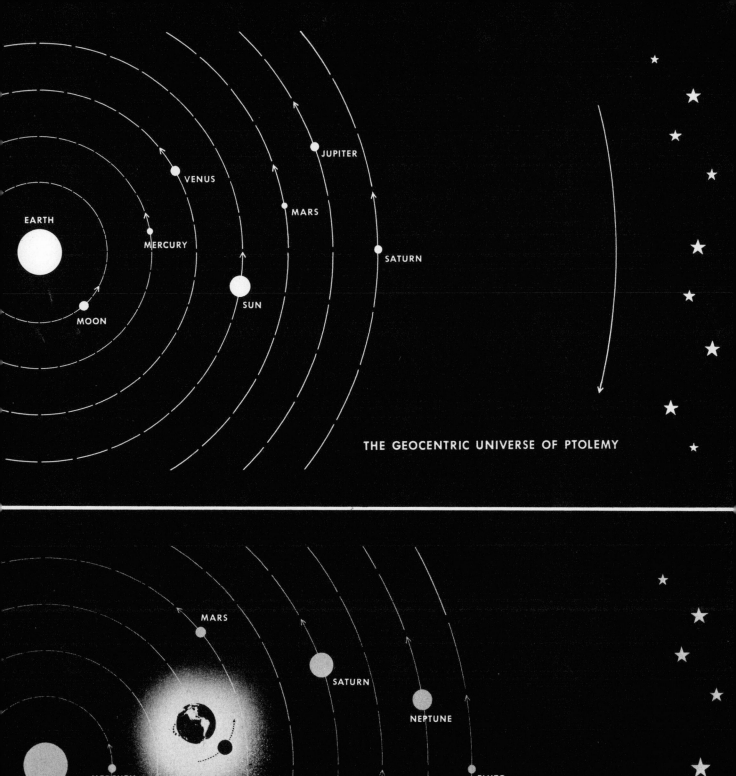

THE GEOCENTRIC UNIVERSE OF PTOLEMY

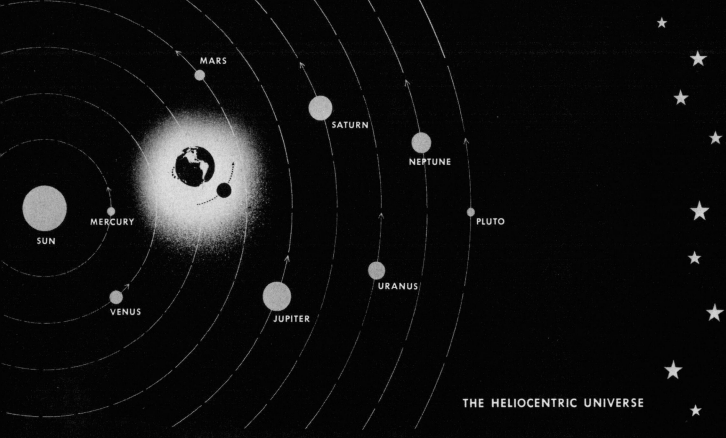

THE HELIOCENTRIC UNIVERSE

SIZE AND SHAPE OF THE EARTH

IF WE COULD somehow travel out into space away from the earth and look back, we would see a huge globe turning steadily beneath us. As the earth turned, we could watch the continents and the oceans moving past. Astronomers call that motion of the earth *rotation*. At the same time, the earth would be moving around the sun, and that motion is its *revolution*. Rotation always refers to the turning of the earth; revolution to the movement around the sun. As we watched, we could also see the earth rotating in the same direction that it was revolving.

The earth's poles are points on the surface at the ends of the axis around which rotation takes place; the equator is an imaginary line midway between the poles dividing the earth into two equal hemispheres. The earth might look like a perfect ball, but careful measurements show that it is not. A line through the center from pole to pole is 7,900 miles long, but another line through the center at the equator is 27 miles longer.

The great forces produced by the earth's rotation have caused some of the material to bulge out along the equator. A perfectly shaped ball is called a sphere, but the earth has the shape of an *oblate spheroid,* which means it is like a sphere, but flattened at the poles. We may think of the earth as a somewhat flattened sphere.

Even so, it might seem to us remarkable that anything as large as the earth could be so nearly a perfect sphere. The highest mountains, reaching upward five and one-half miles, would not seem high at all when compared to the size of the whole earth. The smooth appearance would be more pronounced because much of the surface—seventy-two percent to be exact—is covered with water. The smooth-surfaced globes of the earth that we find in our libraries and schoolrooms are good models of the earth as it might be seen from this point of view in space.

SPHERE

OBLATE SPHEROID

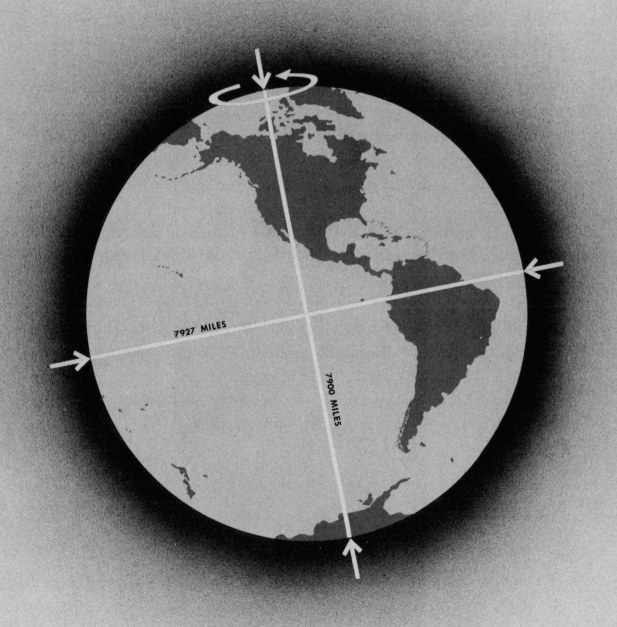

7927 MILES

7900 MILES

LATITUDE AND LONGITUDE

THE EARTH has millions of square miles of surface area. Yet we are able to locate continents, lakes and islands, countries, states and cities, even the homes in which we live. Out on the oceans, and over the oceans, ships and airplanes always know where they are and can radio their positions to the home office.

To make this possible, the earth has been divided by imaginary lines into small blocks. Some of these lines run north and south and pass through the poles. These are called meridians, and the one that goes through Greenwich, England, is called the *prime meridian*. Using the prime meridian as zero dégree, we measure 180 degrees, or half a circle, eastward and westward. Thus we get *longitude,* called east longitude when we measure from Greenwich toward Asia, and west longitude when we measure toward the United States and Canada.

The other lines run around the earth parallel to the equator. These lines are called *parallels of latitude,* or just parallels. All of these parallels, including the equator, make ninety-degree angles with the meridians. We name the equator zero degree and measure latitude north and south from there for a quarter of a circle. The poles are at ninety degrees latitude. From the equator toward the United States, latitude is called north; toward Antarctica it is called south.

On a globe, New York City will be found forty-one degrees north of the equator and seventy-four degrees west of Greenwich, England. Thus, New York is at latitude 41° North and longitude 74° West. Capetown, South Africa, is at latitude 34° South and longitude 18° East.

By using latitude and longitude, we can accurately locate any place on the earth and easily find our way from place to place.

FINDING LATITUDE AND LONGITUDE

WITHOUT ASTRONOMY, it would not be possible to determine latitude and longitude accurately. Tables provided by astronomers give very precise locations for the objects we see in the sky: the sun, the moon, and the stars. Navigators or surveyors then observe these bodies, use the tables provided by astronomers, and translate this information into latitude and longitude.

There are several ways of doing this. For example, the tables tell the navigator the latitude of the point beneath the sun. If the navigator sees the sun directly overhead, when it is highest during the day, then he must be at that latitude. Or suppose he saw the sun exactly ten degrees away from the point overhead, when the sun was highest. Then he would know that his latitude would be ten degrees from the latitude of the point beneath the sun.

Another method very widely used by navigators makes use of a circle of equal altitude. At a given time, the navigator computes the height over the horizon—the altitude—of a star for some known latitude and longitude. The star would have the same altitude from many other places, located in a circle around the point under the star. The known latitude and longitude the navigator used would be on that circle. Then, using a sextant, the instrument pictured here, he would measure the altitude of the star. If it were equal to the one he computed, he would know that he was somewhere on that same circle. If he got a slightly different altitude for the star, he would know that he was on another circle, and the difference between the altitude he measured and the one he computed would tell him how far this other circle was from the first one. Of course, he does not know where on the circle he is, but by repeating the process with several stars, he can find his position where the several circles cross.

Drawing by W. H. Holmquist, American Museum-Hayden Planetarium

THE ROTATION OF THE EARTH

Our EARTH is turning around on its axis, a motion known as rotation. It is also moving around the sun, this motion being called revolution. These two motions of the earth produce effects that can be observed.

First of all, the rotation of the earth causes night and day. Only one side of the earth is lighted by the sun; the other side is dark. As we turn around, we spend part of the time in the darkness and part of the time in the light of the sun. When we are on the bright side, it is daytime; when we are on the dark side, it is night. The duration of what we call a day is the time it takes the earth to rotate once.

Because the earth is rotating, everything we see in the sky—the sun, the moon, the planets, and the stars—must rise and set. As we move around toward the east, it appears that these objects rise in the east, drift westward while they are visible, and set behind the horizon in the west.

Of course, at either one of the earth's poles, stars would not rise or set. They would simply move around in circles as the earth rotated beneath them. To some extent, this can be observed even in the United States. Find the North Star and watch the stars close to it for a few hours. They will seem to be moving around the North Star, as can be seen in the accompanying time-exposure photograph. At the North Pole, where the North Star is over-head, the whole sky would seem to move that way.

The earth is about 24,900 miles around at the equator, and since it rotates once in a day, the velocity at the equator must be over 1,000 miles per hour. Halfway to the North Pole, however, about where Minneapolis, Minnesota is located, the earth is only 17,580 miles in circumference. Minneapolis is circling the pole at a speed of only 732 miles per hour.

Photo: Yerkes Observatory

THE REVOLUTION OF THE EARTH

THE EARTH moves around the sun at a speed of about 18.5 miles per second. Each year, as we go around once, we complete a journey of 586 million miles. The revolution of the earth also produces important effects.

It gives us the calendar. The year is the time it takes the earth to go around the sun once. The earth rotates slightly less than 365¼ turns in the time it takes to go around the sun, so the calendar year has 365 days for three years in a row. Then we have one year of 366 days to make up the quarter extra turn each year. The longer years are our leap years.

Once every hundred years we have to skip the leap year, and then put it back once every four hundred years, to make the average year closer to the actual time the earth takes to go around the sun. The calendar we use now was not possible until astronomers learned exactly how the earth moved, and how long the motions took.

The revolution of the earth is not exactly in a circle, however. We move around the sun in a slightly flattened orbit, called an ellipse. At one point we are closest to the sun, and at another we are farthest.

Early in January we reach the closest point, called *perihelion*—nearest the sun—and then we are about 91½ million miles from it. Early in July we reach *aphelion*—farthest from the sun—about 94½ million miles from it. The earth is revolving a little more rapidly when it is closer and a little more slowly when it is farther away. As a result, there are fewer days in autumn and winter than in spring and summer.

The changing distance from the sun has little to do with the seasons, however. They are caused by something entirely different.

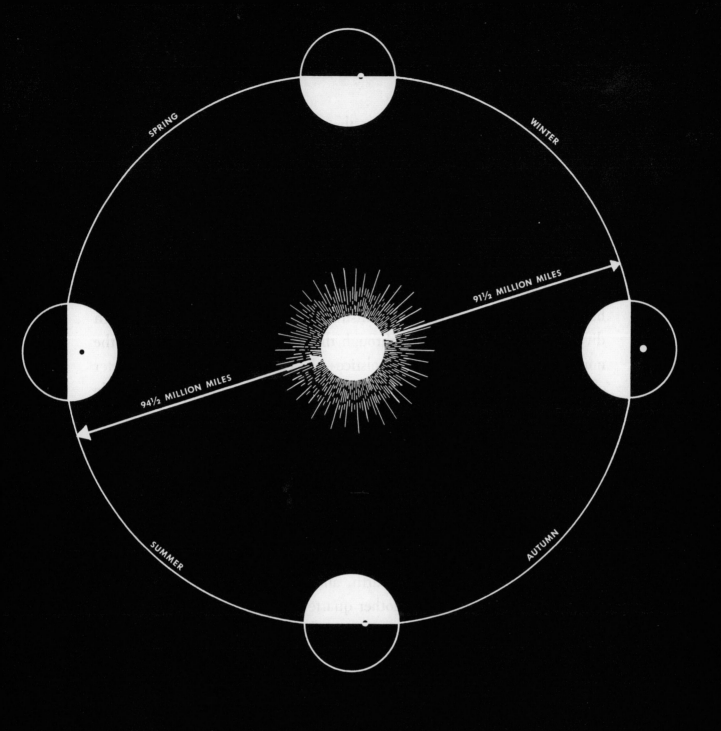

SPRING

WINTER

91½ MILLION MILES

94½ MILLION MILES

SUMMER

AUTUMN

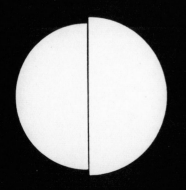

SUN'S DIAMETER AS VIEWED FROM EARTH
AT APHELION (LEFT) AS COMPARED TO
PERIHELION (RIGHT)

THE SEASONS

THE SEASONS come about because the earth is not rotating straight up-and-down with respect to its path around the sun. The line from pole to pole, known as the axis, is tilted, at an angle of about 23½ degrees. The tilt is always the same no matter where the earth is located, and the axis points in the same direction in space, about where the North Star is located. There are changes in the orientation of the axis, but they are not apparent to the casual observer over short periods of time. At the beginning of spring for the Northern Hemisphere—the vernal equinox—the sun is directly over-head at the equator, and there is sunshine at both poles. The line on earth dividing day and night passes through the poles. By the beginning of the northern summer—the summer solstice—the earth has moved one quarter of the way around the sun, and the North Pole is then inclined slightly toward the sun because of the tilt of the axis. The sun is above the Tropic of Cancer, and the North Pole is deep in the sunlit side of the earth.

After another quarter turn, the Northern Hemisphere has autumn, and once more the sun is over the equator—the autumnal equinox. The earth's axis is still tilted the same way, but neither pole is inclined toward the sun. By the beginning of winter, another quarter of the way around the sun, the sun is overhead at the Tropic of Capricorn—the winter solstice. The North Pole is in the dark side of the earth, and the South Pole is in daylight, inclined toward the sun. In another quarter turn, neither pole is inclined toward the sun, and it is again spring in the Northern Hemisphere.

It is the constant tilt of the axis, while the earth moves around the sun, that causes first the North Pole and then the South Pole to be inclined toward the sun and then away from the sun.

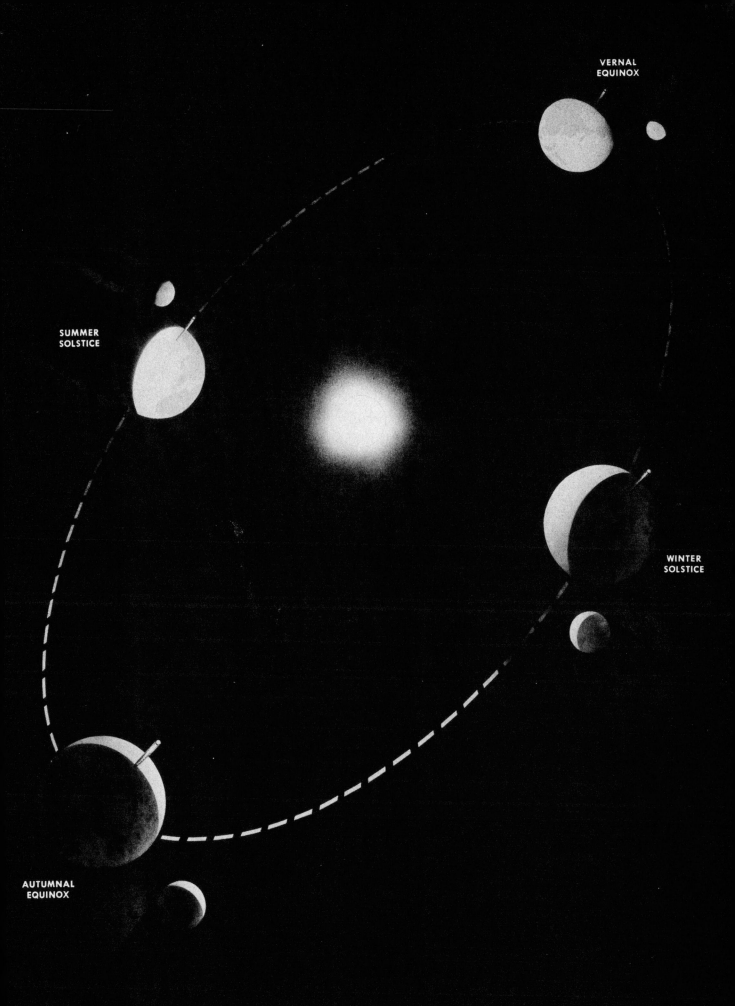

HOW WE KNOW THE EARTH
IS MOVING

THE PEOPLE in ancient times were sure that night and day, the year, and the seasons, came about because the sky and the sun were moving around the earth. It is the earth, rotating and revolving, that causes these things.

Bernard Foucault proved in the year 1851 that the earth is rotating. He used a pendulum, a heavy iron ball at the end of a long wire, suspended from an almost frictionless swivel. Such a pendulum, once set swinging, tends to maintain a fixed direction in space. When Foucault saw that the plane of the pendulum's swing was moving around with respect to the floor beneath, it could only mean that the earth was turning. The experiment has been repeated many times since. The one shown here is in the United Nations headquarters in New York.

There are methods of proving that the earth is moving around the sun. One of these is the parallax method. Look at a distant telephone pole, or a tree, several hundred feet away. Notice what is directly in line with it. Then move to one side and notice that it is no longer aligned the same way. The background changed because you moved. This is the effect known as parallax. Astronomers use the same principle to prove that the earth moves.

The stars are not all at the same distance from the earth. Some are relatively near; others are hundreds of times farther away. The position of a nearby star, seen among the more distant stars in the background, is recorded on photographs taken at six-month intervals. The two photographs show that the star has apparently shifted its position, but this is really due to the motion of earth during the six months.

The slight shift that is observed is as difficult to detect as the diameter of a quarter seen at a distance of four miles. This fine measurement was not possible before excellent telescopes and precision instruments were developed.

Astronomers now use this method to measure the distances to many nearby stars.

Photo: courtesy United Nations

GRAVITATION AND REVOLUTION

AN OBJECT IN MOTION travels in a straight line, unless an outside force prevents it. The earth is traveling through space, but not in a straight line. It is traveling around the sun, and there must be something that causes it to move in this manner. That something is the force of gravitation exerted upon the earth by the sun.

No one knows just what gravitation is. Sir Isaac Newton, a scientist who lived in the 17th century, described it and discovered the laws by which it operates. There is a gravitational attraction between any two objects in the universe, acting from the center of one to the center of the other, tending to pull them together. The amount of the attraction depends on the mass of the two objects (how much material they have in them) and how close together they are.

The earth has 6,600,000,000,000,000,000,000 tons of material in it. The sun has 333,000 times as much. Therefore, the earth is attracted to the center of the sun with a tremendous force. But it cannot fall straight toward the sun's center because it is moving very rapidly. The earth travels about 18½ miles every second; in the same second it also falls a little toward the center of the sun. The distance the earth travels and the amount it falls are exactly enough to balance and keep the earth moving around the sun in its slightly elliptical orbit.

Gravitation holds us on the surface of the earth. Since that attraction is toward the center of the earth, everything on the earth's surface—no matter where—is pulled toward the center, or "down," as we call it. When we weigh ourselves on a scale, we are measuring the force of attraction that the earth's great mass has for us, modified by other factors, one of which is the centrifugal force produced by the earth's rotation. Gravity is the term applied on the surface of the earth to the effect of gravitation plus the special forces which alter it.

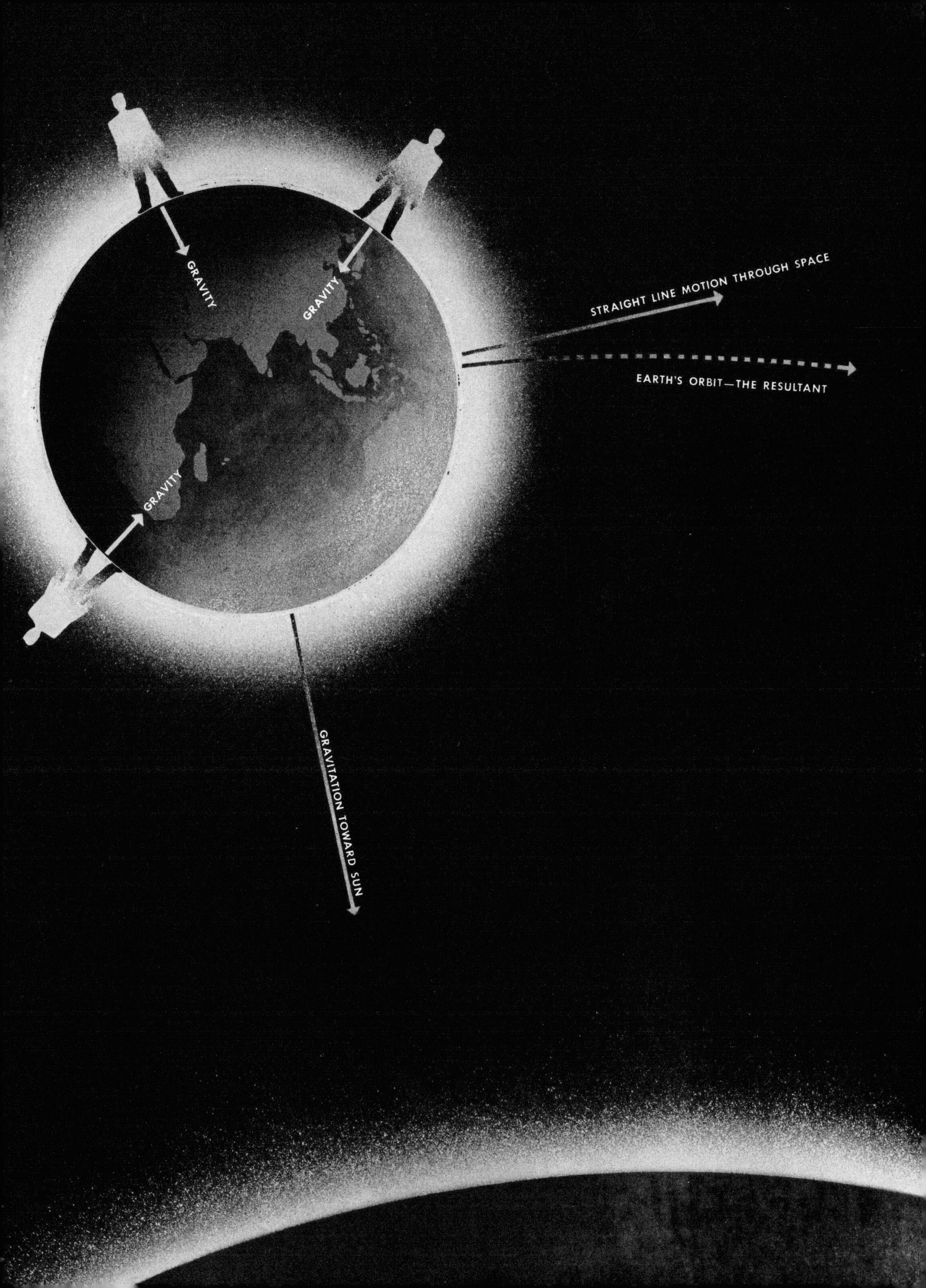

GRAVITY

GRAVITY

GRAVITY

STRAIGHT LINE MOTION THROUGH SPACE

EARTH'S ORBIT—THE RESULTANT

GRAVITATION TOWARD SUN

INSIDE THE EARTH

ABOVE THE EARTH'S SURFACE there is the atmosphere. At the surface, there are water, rocks, soil, and sand. But there is very little experience from which to judge what is found beneath the surface. The deepest mines go down only a few thousand feet, insignificant in relation to the size of the earth. However, it is possible to make a simplified analysis of what the earth's interior is probably like.

The temperature, at least near the surface, increases one degree Fahrenheit for each 60 feet of depth. Earthquake waves, passing through the earth, act as if they were penetrating a liquid when they pass through the central core, but nearer the surface, they behave as if it were solid. Although the density of the earth is 5½, which means that its average weight is about 5½ times as great as the weight of water, the density of the rocks near the surface is only one-half of that.

There seems to be a solid crust of rock at the surface, from 6 to 35 or 40 miles deep. The minerals, ores, soil, sand, and water lie above that. Beneath the crust, there is probably a layer about 2,000 miles thick made up mostly of magnesium, oxygen, and silicon, combined into another form of solid rock. At the center there is a core about 4,000 miles in diameter which may be liquid.

The core is very hot and very dense, and is likely iron and nickel, made even more dense than we know them by the pressure of the rock above. It is hard to understand how it could be liquid at the pressure which exists, despite the high temperature. That is why it is said that the core acts like a liquid, but may not be.

THE ATMOSPHERE

THE LAYER OF GASES surrounding the earth—the atmosphere—is the laboratory for the science of meteorology. Since it is part of the earth, it is also of importance in astronomy.

Air consists of a mixture of many different gases. The most abundant is nitrogen, about 78 percent of the total volume. The most important, as far as we are concerned, is oxygen, about 21 percent of the total. Water vapor and other gases, such as argon, carbon dioxide, xenon, and hydrogen, make up the balance.

Three-fourths of all the air lies within seven miles of the surface, in the region known as the troposphere. Within this region, the temperature normally decreases steadily with height and most of our weather changes take place. Above that, the temperature remains nearly constant, well below freezing, although recent evidence indicates layers of warm and hot air can be found at some high altitudes. This region is called the stratosphere, containing very rarefied air and extending as high as 600 miles above the surface. In recent years the stratosphere has been subdivided into other layers.

Apart from the obvious benefit in giving us the air we breathe, the atmosphere performs other important functions. It serves as a blanket to protect the earth from the sun's heat by day and also to keep the surface warm by night. It filters out harmful radiation from the sun, such as ultraviolet, which would give us severe sunburn. And it shields the surface from particles that come from space, the cosmic rays and meteorites.

The air also produces many phenomena which we consider part of the sky, such as the blue sky of the day, the rainbows and the twilight, the northern lights, and the meteors we see occasionally.

For the astronomer, the atmosphere is a source of frustration and interference. It is so turbulent that even many uncloudy nights with apparently clear skies are actually useless for scientific work. "Bad seeing," as such a condition is known, limits fruitful investigation of the skies to a small percentage of nights. As far as the use of telescopes is concerned, we would be much better off without the air above us.

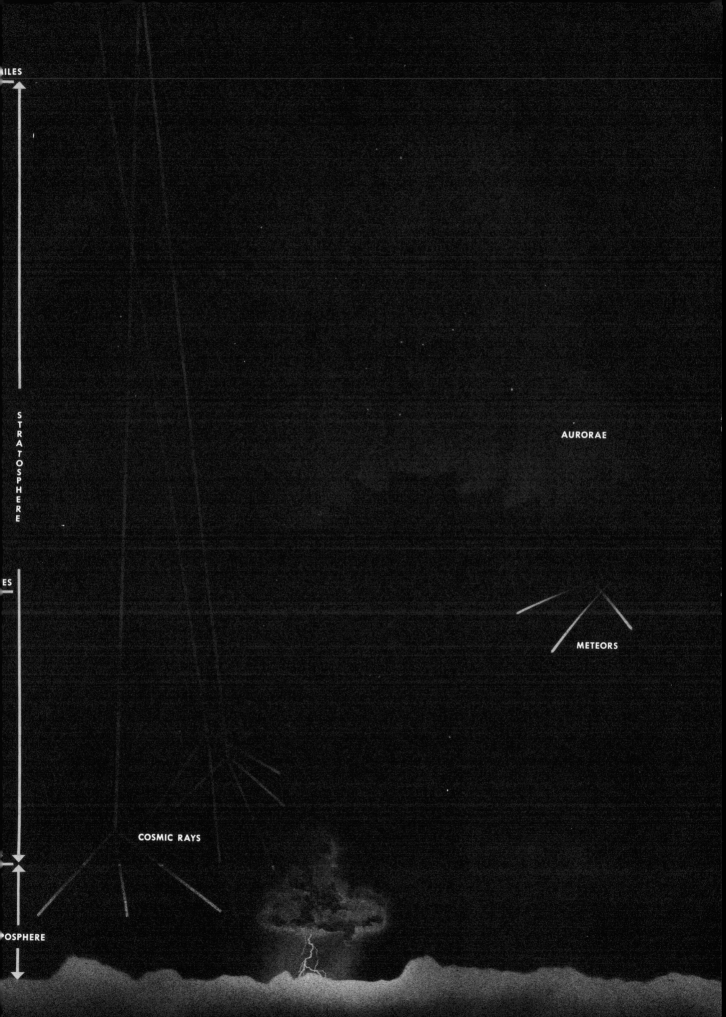

MILES

STRATOSPHERE

ES

AURORAE

METEORS

COSMIC RAYS

OSPHERE

NORTHERN LIGHTS

THE NORTHERN LIGHTS, or *aurora borealis,* is a colorful display of moving lights seen regularly in the skies of arctic regions and frequently farther south in temperate latitudes. The lights may take odd forms and shapes—rays, streamers, arcs, and sometimes curtains or draperies of light, and almost every color can be represented among them. Occasionally they produce only a soft glow, but at other times can be brilliant, filling the entire sky, and bathing the earth with enough light to allow the reading of a newspaper. Sometimes the displays seem stationary, sometimes they shift or sway slowly, and at other times streamers will race across the sky so fast that it may be difficult to follow them.

It is established that the light comes from the gases of the atmosphere, from 60 to 600 miles high. The rarefied gases high above the earth are bombarded by charged particles coming from space, exciting the gases and causing them to glow. The particles causing the northern lights seem to originate in the sun; the displays have been correlated with the disturbances in the sun known as sunspots and flares. It is believed that streams of charged particles are discharged from such solar disturbances. When the streams approach the earth, or when the earth sweeps through them, the particles are deflected by the earth's magnetic field; they concentrate in the regions above the magnetic poles and bombard the upper atmosphere in polar regions. At times of maximum sunspot activity, it can be expected that displays of the aurora will be more frequent.

The northern lights appears most often and most brilliantly from a belt surrounding the north magnetic pole, and decreases from there southward. It can be seen, however, as far south as Florida and Mexico. Just as there is the aurora borealis, the northern lights, there is also an *aurora australis,* southern lights, in the vicinity of the south magnetic pole.

Painting: American Museum-Hayden Planetarium

METEORS

THE SPACE between the planets seems to contain enormous quantities of minute solid particles, traveling around the sun. The earth is constantly running into these particles, and sometimes into clouds or swarms of them. Since the earth is traveling through space at a speed of about 18½ miles per second, and the particles are also traveling rapidly in their orbits around the sun, they fly into the atmosphere at very high speeds, from 10 to 50 miles per second, depending on the direction of their approach.

These small specks of matter become the "shooting stars" or "falling stars" that are seen at night. They appear as thin streaks of light flashing across the sky for a brief time, like the one in this picture. Despite their name, of course, these lights are not really stars at all: they are properly called meteors.

When one of the specks of dust or solid matter comes from space and penetrates the atmosphere, it is traveling so rapidly that the air particles cannot get out of its way fast enough. Friction heats the meteor particle to such a high temperature that it becomes vaporized. The gaseous material from the vaporized meteor strikes particles of the air in its path. Both the meteor gases and the air particles become excited by the energy they absorb in the collisions, and they glow when they release that energy. As a result, the entire path of the visitor from space becomes lighted, and the streak of light appears. Such meteors are about 30 to 100 miles high. The streak of light may average 12 to 15 miles in length.

Several times each year, the earth runs into swarms of particles, and meteor showers result. A number of meteors are seen in the same part of the sky, from only a few to 50 or more per hour. The display may last for several hours, and may occur each night for more than a week. Stray meteors, not part of a shower, can be seen on almost any clear, dark night.

Photo: Yerkes Observatory

FIREBALLS AND BOLIDES

IT HAS BEEN ESTIMATED that billions of solid particles strike the earth's atmosphere daily, but most of them are not seen as meteors. The vast majority are too small and too faint to be seen. Many arrive in the daytime when they cannot be seen. Others strike over the oceans, where there is no one to see them. The meteors that are seen at night represent a very small fraction of the total; they are caused by relatively small particles, possibly weighing about a tenth of an ounce and about as large as the head of a pin.

Once in a while a larger particle strikes the atmosphere—one weighing several ounces or pounds, as large as a baseball or a grapefruit. Such an object leaves a trail far brighter and longer-lasting than the ordinary meteor. It is known as a *fireball*.

The streak of light from a fireball might extend halfway across the sky, and it can be bright enough to be seen clearly in the daytime. At times, the fireball leaves a train of glowing gases behind it, making its trail seem to hang in the sky for several seconds. On rare occasions, fireball trails have remained in the sky for hours, finally dissipating only when the glowing gases were dispersed by winds.

The heat and energy absorbed in these larger particles as they travel rapidly through the air can become so great that they explode, breaking into fragments which might explode again. The fireball is then called a *bolide*. It is even possible to see some of the fragments of a bolide fall to earth after the explosion.

A brilliant fireball or bolide is not seen very often. But when one does appear, especially over heavily-populated areas, it can cause a great deal of excitement, and is often mistaken for strange and impossible things.

Photo: Joseph Klepesta, Prague Observatory

METEORITES

OF THE MANY MILLIONS of meteors and thousands of fireballs, only a few survive their passage through the earth's atmosphere. When they land on the surface, they are known as *meteorites*. Many meteorites have been found, and some are on display in museums throughout the world.

There are three kinds of meteorites, according to their composition. Some are metallic, made up of iron, with some nickel, and minute traces of other elements. Others are rocky in structure, with small amounts of iron and nickel. Still others are combinations of those two types. Almost every chemical element known on earth has been found in meteorites, and no element has been found that we do not have on earth. From a study of meteorites which came from space, it seems that matter both on the earth and in space must be made from the same ingredients.

It is usually hard to tell whether an object is a meteorite or whether it is an ordinary clinker, rock, or piece of slag. A fragment of natural iron found on the earth is immediately suspected of being a meteorite, because iron does not occur naturally on the earth's surface. To be certain, however, the object must be tested for nickel and for the peculiar crystalline structure in the iron which is characteristic of iron meteorites. Stony meteorites are somewhat more difficult to detect, and it usually requires the attention of an expert to be certain.

The largest meteorite known lies half-buried in the earth near Grootfontein, southwest Africa. It is estimated to weigh between 50 and 75 tons. The largest one on display is in The American Museum-Hayden Planetarium in New York City. It weighs a little over 34 tons. Admiral Robert E. Peary brought it from Cape York, Greenland, in 1897. Recently it has been placed on a specially-made scale, so that visitors can actually read on a dial the weight of this huge object from outer space.

Photo: American Museum-Hayden Planetarium

METEOR CRATERS

Near flagstaff, arizona, not far from U. S. Highway 66, there is a scar on the landscape that must have been caused by a large cosmic missile coming out of the sky thousands of years ago. It left a crater four-fifths of a mile in diameter and about 600 feet in depth from the crater floor to the surrounding ridge. Though many holes have been bored into the earth beneath the crater in an attempt to find the body of the meteorite, it has never been located. Recently, additional holes have been drilled south of the crater on the theory that the meteor came in at an angle from the north and buried itself deep in the rocks to the south. However, it has not been found.

Thousands of fragments of meteoric iron, more than have been found on the rest of the earth's surface, have been collected near the crater. Their crystalline form and nickel-iron content tell us with certainty that they are meteorites. Their distribution resulted from the same explosive impact that caused the crater, for the greatest number have been found close to it. Perhaps these fragments are all that we should expect to find. Maybe the force of the explosion was so tremendous that most of the material was vaporized. If so, we may never expect to find the huge meteorite that caused Meteor Crater, Arizona.

There are other craters, too—a large one in Canada, a large one in Australia, and several along the eastern coast of the United States—that were probably caused by meteors. There may have been many others that were run over by the great glaciers that moved across the northern continents long ago. It is even possible that the earth once had a surface as scarred as that of the moon, but the many changes on the earth during the past several million years have erased all but a very few of them.

Photo: American Museum-Hayden Planetarium

CHAPTER II

THE ASTRONOMER'S INSTRUMENTS

THE ACCOMPLISHMENTS of modern astronomy would not be possible but for the highly specialized and important tools that have been developed for probing the heavens. Less than four centuries ago, men could only study the sky and the objects found in it with their eyes. Today, however, the well-equipped astronomical observatory is one of the finest and most elaborate installations of science.

Many sciences and technologies have contributed their share to the instruments which astronomers now use—photography, chemistry, optics, spectroscopy, electronics, and others. Accuracy is vital, for the faint energy received on earth from distant planets, stars, and galaxies contains the only evidence available from which to determine their size, distance, nature, and significance.

THE FIRST TELESCOPE

JAN LIPPERSHEY was the proprietor of a shop in Holland that specialized in the manufacture of eyeglasses. One day in the year 1608, one of his apprentices was toying with different kinds of lenses, curious about the manner in which light was distorted and bent as it passed through them. Very likely it was only chance that led him to hold two of these lenses apart and look through them toward a distant object which then appeared larger and nearer. Without knowing what he was doing, he had invented the telescope!

Galileo Galilei, a physicist and astronomer from the University of Padua in Italy, heard of the discovery and realized how valuable this new device could be for looking into the heavens. He fitted two lenses into opposite ends of a lead tube and made a crude telescope that magnified objects three times. After much experimenting, and many improvements, he finally was able to build an instrument that made objects appear thirty times larger than to the unaided eye.

Galileo's friends in Venice were excited; the merchants of the city were amazed that ships approaching the harbor could be seen with a telescope at a much greater distance. It was the view of the skies, though, that convinced Galileo that he had actually opened a new chapter in the study of astronomy. For the first time he saw that the Milky Way was composed of so many stars that they defied counting; that there were markings on the moon—mountains, "seas," valleys, and craters; that Saturn had an appearance unlike any other object; that Jupiter had four great satellites; and that Venus went through phases like the moon.

The changing appearance of Venus proved that it was going around the sun, not the earth. And the view of Jupiter with its moons, a small-scale system not unlike the sun and its planets, proved once and for all that the Copernican view of the planets could be correct, and that we live in a "solar system" that is dominated by the sun and not by the earth.

Galileo and some merchants from Venice
Photo: courtesy Bausch & Lomb Optical Co.

46

REFRACTING TELESCOPES

GALILEO'S SIMPLE OPTIC TUBE was a *refractor*. In this type of instrument, the light passes through a lens at the front end of the telescope, and is refracted to a focus near the bottom of the tube. The lens is called the *objective* and is the most expensive and most important part of the instrument.

For many years after the development of the telescope, refractors were made larger and better, but trouble was encountered. A simple lens does not refract all colors of light by the same amount. Each color comes to a focus in a slightly different plane, making it impossible to get sharp images. The larger the lens, the more annoying becomes the "chromatic aberration," as the color breakdown is called. To avoid it, telescope tubes were made longer and longer, and many of the instruments became so unwieldy that they could be used only with difficulty. Special correcting lenses were developed to reduce this trouble, but they are difficult to make and quite expensive and it is impossible to eliminate the aberration completely.

The largest of the modern refracting-type telescopes is located at the Yerkes Observatory in Williams Bay, Wisconsin. The large, light-gathering lens is 40 inches in diameter, and the tube of the telescope is 63 feet long. Some of the finest pictures of the planets, the moon, and the Milky Way have been made with this instrument, for the special value of the refractor lies in the clarity and fine detail of the image at the focal plane. Many of the important research contributions in the field of astronomy have come from the astronomers at the Yerkes Observatory.

The second largest refractor is the 36-inch telescope at the Lick Observatory of the University of California on Mount Hamilton, southeast of San Francisco. There are more than twenty other refractors over twenty-four inches in diameter.

Photo: Yerkes Observatory

REFLECTING TELESCOPES

THE WORLD'S LARGEST TELESCOPES are reflectors, for they are more simple to make than refractors, are completely free of chromatic aberration, and can often be adapted more readily to the special demands of the astronomer. The objective in this type of telescope is a mirror placed at the bottom of the tube. Light enters through the open upper end, travels to the mirror, and is then reflected to some convenient place for observing.

The Newtonian reflector has a small secondary mirror placed near the open end to divert the light to the side of the instrument, where the eyepiece (or ocular) is fastened. This is the most common design. In the Cassegrain reflector, a hole is cut in the large mirror at the bottom of the telescope, and a small mirror of special design (hyperbolic) focuses the light to a point under the objective near the end of the tube. There are other variations of the reflector, and some telescopes are designed to allow use of several of them.

The 200-inch reflector of the Hale telescope on Palomar Mountain is the largest. Because of its gigantic size, it can gather more light than any other telescope and has been used to find and identify faint celestial objects at fantastic distances. It is not often used for "nearby" objects, such as the planets, because its special worth depends on its light-gathering power.

The next three largest reflectors are also in the United States. The 120-inch is a new companion to the 36-inch refractor at the Lick Observatory. The 100-inch Hooker telescope, operated by the California Institute of Technology (which also operates the Hale telescope) is on Mount Wilson near the city of Los Angeles. The 82-inch reflector of the McDonald Observatory is at Mt. Locke, in western Texas.

Photo: courtesy Mt. Wilson and Palomar Observatories

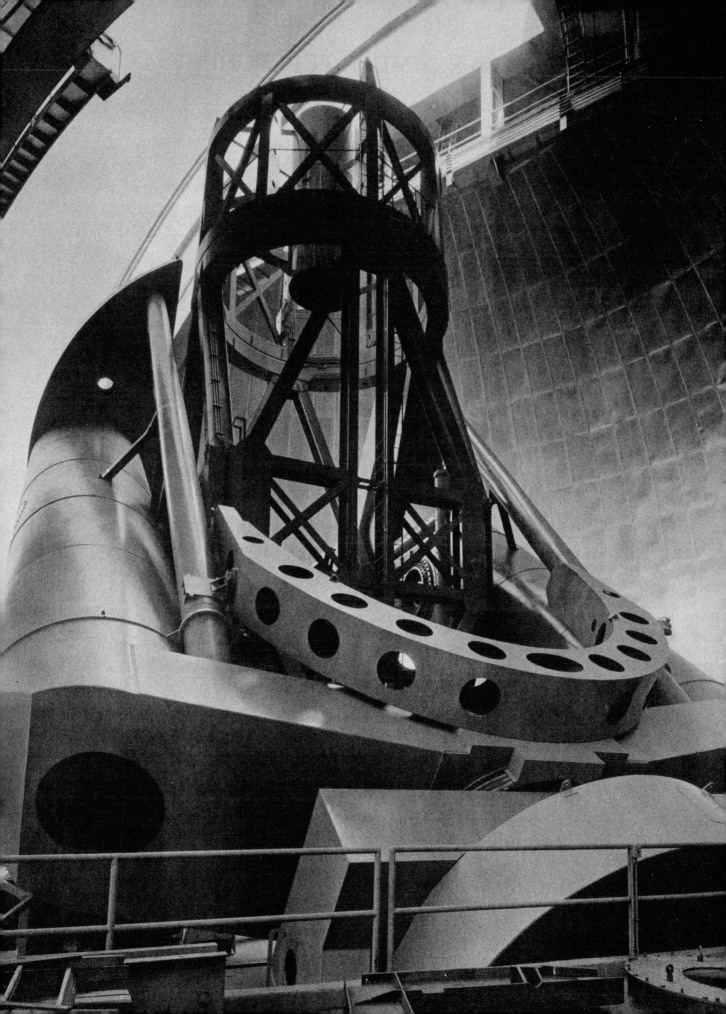

THE SCHMIDT TELESCOPE

ONE OF THE NEWEST astronomical instruments is listed among the most valuable tools of the astronomer. It is the Schmidt camera telescope, suggested in 1930 by the German, Bernhard Schmidt. The Schmidt camera consists of three essential parts: a spherical mirror at the bottom end of the tube, a special "correcting lens" at the end where the light enters, and a curved photographic plateholder between the other two. The principle is simple enough, but the correcting lens is extremely difficult to construct, for it must affect the incoming light differently in the different sections of its area.

This type of instrument solves one of the most difficult of photographic problems, that of taking a picture of a large area but with fine detail. The Schmidt camera can combine the light-gathering power of a large mirror with the larger viewing area of a smaller instrument. It covers a much larger area of the sky than a conventional telescope of the same size, and it can produce sharp images of faint objects over the whole area of the picture it produces.

The pictures taken with the Schmidt are studied carefully in the laboratory. If the astronomer notices something that arouses his curiosity, a conventional telescope which photographs in much greater detail can be directed to the part of the sky indicated. Many new galaxies have been located and studied in this manner. We might think of the Schmidt telescope as part of a team: it does the scouting, and the large reflector or refractor closes in to investigate more fully. In this way the 48-inch Schmidt telescope at Palomar Mountain does the scouting for the 200-inch Hale telescope.

Recently, the 48-inch Schmidt telescope has proved its merit by producing a series of charts covering the entire sky visible from southern California. This *Palomar Sky Atlas,* published in 1955, contains more extensive detail than any survey of the skies previously available. Now it is a valuable guide for astronomers all over the world, but in future years it may be even more valuable as a permanent record of the skies as they were in our age. Astronomers will undoubtedly use it as a reference to compare the heavens of the future to the skies as they once appeared.

Photo: courtesy Mt. Wilson and Palomar Observatories

TOWER TELESCOPES

WHEN THE TUBE of a telescope is long, the image in the focal plane is large. Since it is helpful to have a large image for studying the planets, the moon and especially the sun, many attempts have been made to construct telescopes of long focal length. Unfortunately, however, the length of the telescope is limited because if it is made too long, it tends to sag, or, if supported so it won't sag, it becomes so large and cumbersome that it is difficult to use.

Not far from the 100-inch Hooker reflector on Mt. Wilson in California is a tower telescope that has been designed to overcome this problem. The tower is 150 feet high with a combination of mirrors mounted at the top which reflects sunlight down the enclosed central case. The reflected light, after passing through a 12-inch lens at the top of the tower, comes to a focus at the observer's location on the ground. In effect, the stationary tower is the tube of an extremely long telescope— so long, in fact, that the image of the sun is 17 inches in diameter at the focal plane. It provides a fine means of studying the detail of the sun's surface.

There is a pit seventy-five feet deep under the tower. At the bottom is a grating for dispersing the sun's light and reflecting it to a focus at ground level. This is a built-in spectroscope which permits the astronomer on duty to study the solar spectrum in addition to the 17-inch solar image in the focal plane.

There are two other "coelostat" telescopes at Mt. Wilson, one in a tower 60 feet high, and another in a shed parallel to the ground. In both, the rotating mirror (coelostat) is the only moving part, and the long telescope "tubes" remain rigidly fixed in place.

Photo: courtesy Mt. Wilson and Palomar Observatories

THE SPECTROSCOPE

In 1666, ISAAC NEWTON discovered that white light is composed of all the colors in the rainbow from the long-wave-length red at one extreme to the short-wave-length blue at the other. Orange, yellow, and green—in that order—appear at their proper locations between. Later, Fraunhofer, Ångström, and others learned that the specific relationships among these colors, and among the "dark lines" which appeared on the color spectrum under certain conditions, reveal a great deal about the source of the light.

When light from a star is caused to pass through a prism of specially-formed glass, or to reflect on a grating of carefully prepared metal, the color breakdown takes place. The band of colors produced is known as a spectrum. The chemical elements contained in the light source display a special light pattern that shows up among these colors of the spectrum. By comparing the light pattern from the stars with light from a known source, it is possible to identify the elements represented in the spectrum of the starlight, and thus to learn important facts about the star that is emitting the light.

The spectroscope is the instrument used for this kind of light analysis. It is placed at the eyepiece end of a telescope. It consists of a *slit* to give sharpness and greater resolving power, a *collimator* to render light rays from the slit parallel, then the *prism,* and finally a small telescope to focus the colored light on a screen. If a camera replaces the view telescope and screen, then the device is called a *spectrograph.* Modern astrophysics, the study of the internal and physical nature of stars, depends heavily on these devices.

This photograph shows the 82-inch reflecting telescope of the McDonald Observatory with a spectrograph attached at the Cassegrain focus. This illustrates the common practice of using modern great telescopes in conjunction with accessory astronomical equipment.

Photo: Yerkes Observatory

THE RADIO TELESCOPE

THE RADIO TELESCOPE is the newest device for studying the characteristics of the stars, some of the planets, the sun, and interstellar gas. It can be used for exploring parts of the sky where nothing can be seen, but where something very likely exists. With it, for example, it is possible to probe beyond the dark obscuring clouds of the Milky Way. It can be used by day as well as by night. Most important, it provides information about the radio energy section of the spectrum; our knowledge is no longer limited to the kind of energy that comes to us as visible light.

One type of instrument consists of a large reflecting screen for receiving the radio signals from space, a dipole or horn for collecting the energy reflected to it by the screen, an electronic system for amplifying the energy, and a mechanical device for recording the intensity of the radio "noise" on a graph. The reflecting screen may be made of sheet metal, ordinary wire mesh, or just plain wire laid out over a series of supports, depending on the use of the instrument. Though this type of radio telescope uses the same principles of physical optics as the regular telescope, it presents new problems, often more severe.

The study of radio energy from the skies has been going on for only a few years but already some fascinating information has been acquired. As expected, the part of the Milky Way where so many stars are concentrated has a high noise level. Stars alone seem not to make too great a radio impression, but ionized gases which are the remnants of a former supernova (such as the Crab Nebula) are quite intense as radiators. Distant galaxies emit radio-frequency radiation, but so do some of our neighbors in the solar system.

The largest radio telescope is a huge 250-foot bowl or "dish," as many call it, at Jodrell Bank in England. There are others in Australia, Holland, the United States, and many other places. One of the red, white, and blue "bowl" receivers of the National Bureau of Standards near Boulder, Colorado is pictured on the opposite page. This and its two mates automatically track the sun daily from sunrise to sunset, making continuous recordings of solar radio noise emissions.

Photo: courtesy National Bureau of Standards

THE PLANETARIUM

A PLANETARIUM is a special type of educational institution devoted to the teaching of astronomy. There are large ones in about thirty of the major cities of the world; seven of these are in the United States—in Chicago, Philadelphia, Los Angeles, New York, Pittsburgh, Chapel Hill, and San Francisco. There will soon be others in Boston, Flint, and at the Air Force Academy in Colorado. All are large enough to accommodate several hundred people. In addition, there are many smaller classroom-size installations.

At the center of a hemispherical dome in each planetarium is a projector which, through its many lenses, lamps, motors, and gears, can reproduce the sky on the inside of the dome as it should appear from any place on earth for thousands of years past or future. Special projectors simulate the colors of the sky, comets, "shooting stars," and clouds of all kinds.

The Zeiss planetarium projector is the best known and most common, though the Spitz projector, made in the United States, is now also available. The instrument looks like a dumbbell, with the globes at the ends fitted with equipment for projecting the stars. The sun, moon, and planets each have individual cages in the central part of the device, and all are related to each other by gears which cause them to move and produce light images on the dome in the proper places among the stars. A complete rotation of the earth can be demonstrated in four minutes, and a year of motion of the sun, moon, and planets can be completed in just seven seconds. Latitude and precession changes can also be shown.

With this kind of visual aid, astronomical topics of current interest can be presented and interpreted to the public. Such features as *Exploring the Milky Way, From Here to Infinity, Our Neighbor Worlds, From Galileo to Palomar,* and *The Star of Bethlehem,* are offered. Some planetaria also offer courses of instruction in astronomy and navigation.

Photo: American Museum-Hayden Planetarium

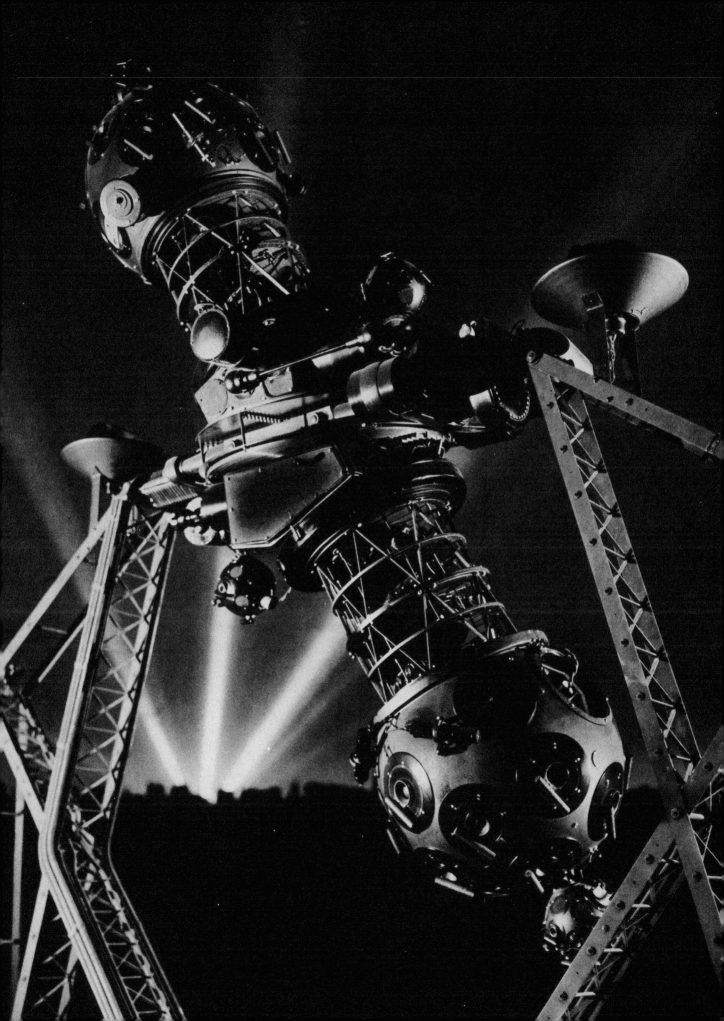

CHAPTER III

THE MOON—EARTH SATELLITE

THE TOTAL INFLUENCE of the moon upon the course of human history is difficult to evaluate. It contributes light to the nighttime, and thereby has aided travelers of all times. Its movements in the heavens are quite rapid and easily observed, so that it gave men the earliest means of keeping track of long periods of time. Primitive calendars were based on cycles of the moon, and even calendars of today bear its influence. Throughout the history of human events, it has inspired song and story, poetry and prose, and has contributed to our most valuable literary art.

Most directly, however, its effect is felt in the tides. Though the moon is not of great mass compared to the vast majority of celestial objects, it is so close to the earth that its tide-producing force far exceeds that of even the massive sun. Lunar tides occur in the solid earth and in the atmosphere, though their effects on the earth's motion and the weather patterns are not well understood. It is in the waters of the earth and their periodic ebb and flow that the tides of the moon and their results are most obvious, controlling the course of history, exploration, military conquest, and commerce.

Only a small world in space, with a diameter about one-fourth that of the earth, the moon is the brightest object of the night, second brightest of all we see in the sky. Its importance lies in being the nearest to the earth of all celestial bodies.

THE MOON—OUR NEAREST NEIGHBOR

THE SECOND BRIGHTEST OBJECT in the sky, and the brightest of the nighttime, is the earth's closest neighbor, the moon. It is a dead and forbidding world that circles around the earth about a quarter of a million miles away, much as the earth circles around the sun. No other large celestial body approaches so close.

In some ways, the moon is like the earth. It has little light or heat, except that which it receives from the sun. We see it because it reflects some of the sunlight that falls on it. Even so, it is a very poor reflector; only seven percent of the sunlight it receives is reflected and causes it to become visible. The surface of the moon is completely solid. Unlike the earth, it has no water, and there is no significant atmosphere.

The diameter of the moon—2,163 miles—is about one-fourth that of the earth. The mass is only one and one-quarter percent of the earth's mass. Because it is much smaller than the earth, gravity on the moon would be less than gravity on earth. On the surface of the moon we would weigh only 1/6 of our weight on the earth's surface.

Considering its influence upon the lives of people, animals, and plants on the earth, the moon is the second most important object in the sky. It is the illuminator of the night. It is responsible for the month as a calendar unit, and, working with the sun, it produces the important rise and fall in the earth's waters—the tides. In ancient times, calendars depended solely upon the moon, and lunar calendars are still used by many people for religious purposes. The dates of Easter and Passover are determined by the motions of the moon.

Because the moon goes around the earth instead of around the sun, it is not a planet, even though it resembles the planets in many respects. It is a satellite, one of 31 in our solar system.

ONE OF THE MOST obvious things about the moon is the manner in which it continuously changes its appearance. These changes are known as the phases of the moon, and they occur in their familiar pattern as the moon revolves around the earth in the same direction in which the earth revolves around the sun.

Once in about each four weeks, the moon is in the same direction as the sun. It is then invisible in the daylight sky because the dark side faces the earth; the side reflecting sunlight is turned away.

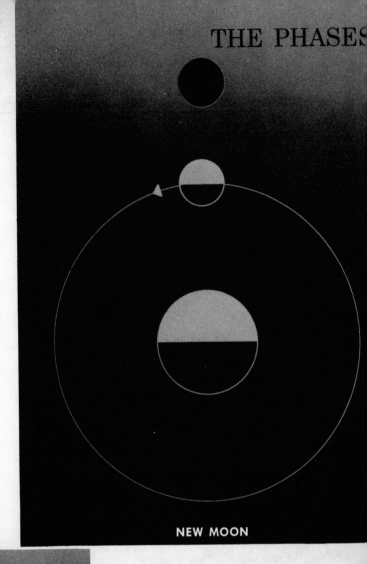

NEW MOON

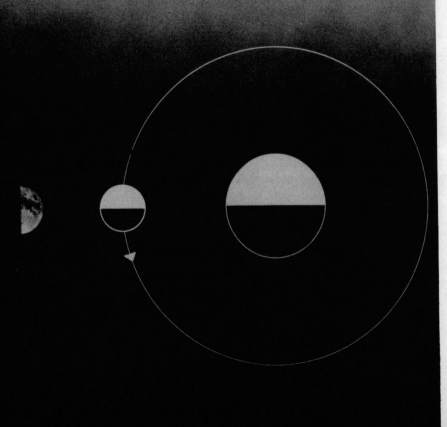

FIRST-QUARTER MOON

That is the new moon, rising and setting at the same time as the sun. About a week later, the moon has moved one-fourth of the way around the earth and it is one-quarter of the sky eastward from the sun. At this time one-half of the lighted surface can be seen and it is the first-quarter moon. This is the moon seen in the afternoon, and over in the western sky during the early part of the night.

In about one more week, the moon moves another one-quarter of the way around the earth and is then halfway around the sky from the sun. The whole lighted surface of the moon can be seen from the earth, and it is called the full moon. Since it is opposite to the sun, it rises and sets opposite. The full moon is the bright, fully round moon that rises when the sun goes down and stays in the sky all night long.

After one more week, the moon is three-quarters of the way around the earth. Once again half of the lighted surface can be seen. This is the last-quarter moon, rising in the east about

FULL MOON

LAST-QUARTER MOON

midnight, and remaining in the sky during the morning hours.

Although the moon takes 27⅓ days to go around the earth, it takes about 29½ days to go through these phases, because the earth is moving around the sun in the meantime. The 29½-day period of the moon's phases was the month in the ancient calendars. The length of the months in our modern calendar have been changed so that they no longer correspond to the period of the moon through its cycle.

THE FACE OF THE MOON

THE MOON is one of very few objects in the sky on which we can clearly see features without the aid of a telescope. With our eyes alone we can distinguish the prominent dark markings and the great bright areas that make up the face of the "man in the moon." Persons with very good eyes can sometimes make out some of the craters.

At one time it was thought that the dark areas were oceans and seas; their names still include the Latin *mare* which means sea. Modern telescopes show that they are dry, flat plains, stretching across the moon's surface. One of the largest, Mare Imbrium, the Sea of Showers, is in the central region of this picture. It is nearly circular, about 750 miles in diameter, and ringed round by high, rugged mountains. Although it appears at the bottom of the picture, it is actually in the northern half of the moon. Pictures taken with a telescope are inverted. The top of the moon you see in the sky would be the bottom of the picture.

There are several craters visible on the floor of Mare Imbrium. The largest one is Archimedes, a little above and to the left of center in the picture. Its diameter is about 50 miles, and its walls are estimated to be nearly one and one-half miles high. This is not the largest crater on the moon. Clavius, near the very bright region at the top of the picture on page 64, measures about 145 miles in diameter.

Some areas on the moon are so filled with craters, many superimposed on the ruins of others, that they present an incredibly rough surface. Note the crater at the edge of Mare Imbrium, in the shadows just below center at the left side of the photograph. The several smaller craters on the walls and on the floor must have been formed at some time after the larger one.

Contrast the rugged appearance of Autolycus and Aristillus, the large prominent craters to the left of Archimedes, with the smooth, dark floor of Archimedes.

Photo: Mt. Wilson and Palomar Observatories; 100-inch photograph

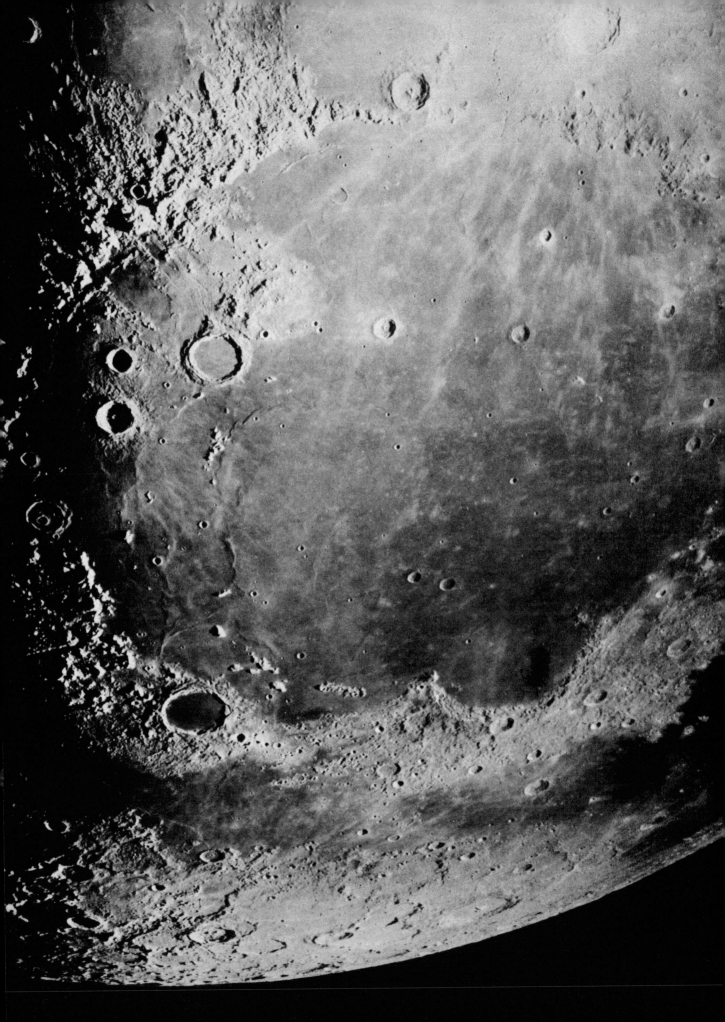

CLOSE-UP OF THE MOON

IN THIS PICTURE, we are brought to a point within a few hundred miles of the moon's surface. We are looking at the region surrounding the crater Copernicus, which also appears in the upper right-hand corner of the photograph on the previous page. The picture portrays a typical section of the moon and many of the features that mark its surface.

Copernicus, at the center of the picture, is a crater 56 miles in diameter. Its walls slope gradually upward through a series of terraces to a height of about 12,000 feet above the floor. The center of the crater is not smooth; it rises in a mountain with several peaks. To the left of Copernicus there is another large and very beautiful crater, called Eratosthenes. It seems to be younger than Copernicus because of its sharp and rugged features. The crater is 38 miles in diameter, and its walls rise very sharply to 16,000 feet. The mountain in the center of the crater has another small crater pit at its summit. There are many other small craters in this area. The shadows of the crater walls and the mountains, cast by sunlight, make it possible to measure their height.

To the left of Eratosthenes there are several mountains, the beginning of the range known as the Apennines. The mountains just below Copernicus are the Carpathians.

A series of bright markings radiate outward from Copernicus, crossing mountains, craters, and the flat darkness of the plain. These are called *rays* and are found around many of the moon's craters. They suggest that the craters were formed by explosions, scattering fragments outward to form the rays. The long, crooked cracks in the surface between Copernicus and Eratosthenes are *rills* and may have been caused by tremors on the moon similar to earthquakes.

No one knows what caused the craters on the moon, or the other features. Many theories have been offered: volcanic eruptions and meteor impacts are the favorites. But none fully satisfies the great variety and numbers of the formations observed.

Photo: courtesy Mt. Wilson and Palomar Observatories; 100-inch photograph

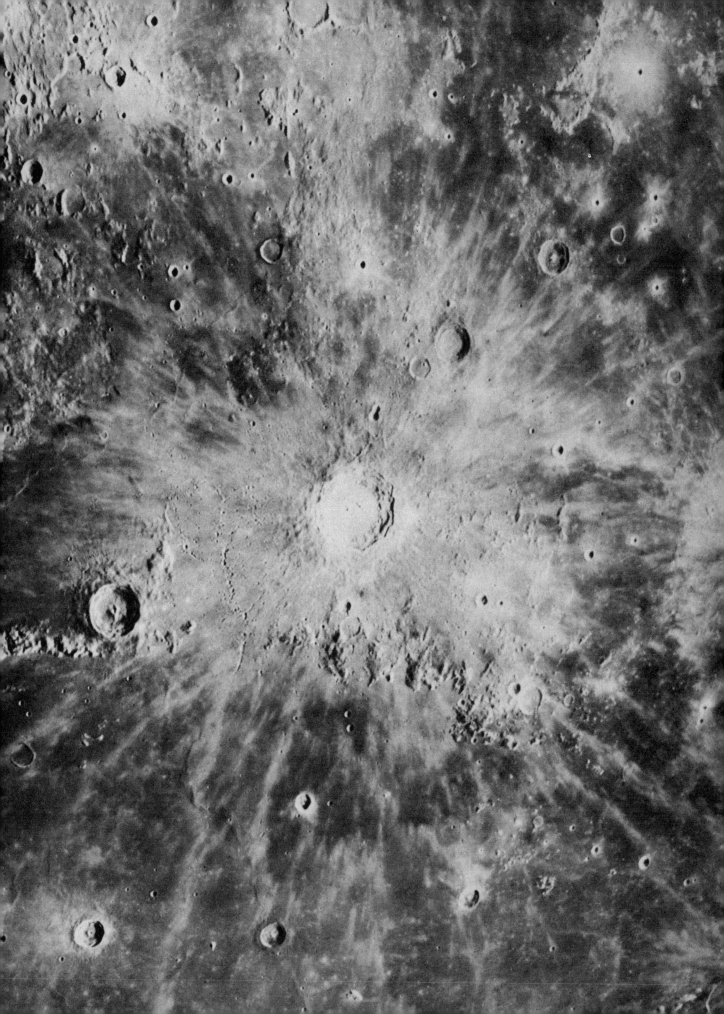

A DAY ON THE MOON

IT IS WELL KNOWN that the same side of the moon always faces the earth. When the moon is new, the side facing us is in darkness. At full moon, the same side is fully lighted by the sun. Then at the next new moon it is dark again. The moon must be rotating with respect to the sun, because the side facing earth is dark at one time and bright at another. Observation proves that the moon rotates once in the same time that it revolves around the earth, 27⅓ days. A day on the moon would last for about four weeks of earth time.

Day and night on the moon would be quite different from ours. They would be longer, of course, but many other differences would result from the absence of atmosphere. The most startling would be the appearance of the sky. With no air to scatter sunlight, the sky of the moon would be dark both day and night, and the stars could be seen all the time. There would be no rainbow, no twilight, no glow in the sky at sunrise or sunset.

Meteors could not be seen as "shooting stars." It would be hotter by day, without air to shield the surface from the sun's rays. It would become much colder at night, without air to serve as a blanket and keep the surface heat from radiating into space.

A day on the moon begins with a sudden brightening of the upper part of the mountains and crater walls and then the whole surface, as the sun comes above the horizon. The sky remains black, sun and stars visible together. Within a few hours, the temperature of the surface rises above the boiling point of water, and remains that way for most of the two-week day. The glare of reflected sunlight and the heat from the surface would be unbearable; relief could be found only in the shadows of rocks and craters.

With the sunset, darkness comes quickly, first to the surface and then to the tops of the crater walls. The surface rapidly loses the heat it has collected in the daytime. It remains cold until sunrise, two weeks later.

Photo: American Museum-Hayden Planetarium

TIDES AND THE MOON

ANYONE who lives near the seashore or who has visited beaches knows that the level of the earth's waters is changing very regularly. It will generally reach a high level twice each day and a low level twice each day. These changes are known as the *tides*. There is no doubt that the principal factor in causing the tides is the moon. The time of moonrise comes, on the average, about 50 minutes later each day. A similar lag can be observed in the times of high and low tides.

Tides are caused by the difference in the moon's gravitational attraction for different parts of the earth. As a result, there tends to be a bulge in the water under the moon and another bulge in the water on the side of the earth opposite to the moon. These two bulges cause the two high tides that come each day.

The sun also produces tides, but of less magnitude than those of the moon. At certain times, however, the tides of the moon and the sun work together, and the resulting range in tide can be much greater than normal. These are *spring tides,* and they come twice each month, at new moon and at full moon. At the time of first-quarter moon and last-quarter moon, the tidal range is less than normal, and these are *neap tides*.

The distance between the earth and moon also affects the tides. Once in about each four weeks the moon is closest to the earth, at *perigee*. This also causes the tides to be greater—higher high tides and lower low tides. When the moon is farthest from the earth, a position known as *apogee*, tides are less than normal. Sometimes perigee comes at a time of new or full moon. Then the increase in tides from perigee is added to the spring tide, and exceptionally high tides result.

The shape and uneven character of the earth's surface affect the tides. They usually come later than they would if the earth were completely water-covered. In some places on earth there are only one high tide and one low tide each day; in other places they tend to have unusually great ranges. Along the west coast of England, tides of more than 30 feet occur. In the Bay of Fundy, in southeastern Canada, the tides sometimes raise the water to heights of 50 feet.

Photo: courtesy Nova Scotia Film Bureau

AN ECLIPSE OF THE MOON

ECLIPSES are caused by shadows. Both the moon and the earth are solid objects, with long. cone-shaped shadows pointing away from the sun. During an eclipse of the sun, the shadow of the moon falls on earth and can actually be seen passing swiftly across the earth's surface. During an eclipse of the moon, it is the moon that passes through the shadow of the earth.

An eclipse of the moon does not take place every month, because the moon's path around the earth is tilted with respect to the earth's orbit. Most of the time the moon passes a little above or below the earth's shadow. As often as three times a year, however, it can pass through the shadow. Everyone who can see the moon can also see an eclipse of the moon. Thus, lunar eclipses are observed more often, even though eclipses of the sun occur more frequently.

An eclipse of the moon may take several hours to be completed. It always occurs when the moon is full, opposite to the sun, because the earth's shadow is opposite the sun. At the beginning of the eclipse, darkness encroaches on the eastern edge of the moon, and then a dark, curved shadow appears to creep across the face of the full moon. The part of the moon in the shadow remains visible, but it takes on a peculiar coppery-red tone.

The light and color can be seen because the shadow of the earth is not completely dark. Sunlight, falling on the earth's atmosphere, is bent around by the air into the shadow. Most of the blue light is scattered or absorbed in the earth's atmosphere, or is lost in space between the earth and moon. The reddish hues are bent enough to fall on the eclipsed surface.

The eclipse ends as the moon leaves the earth's shadow, passing into sunlight, to become the bright full moon once more.

Photo: A. Rota, American Museum-Hayden Planetarium

AN ECLIPSE OF THE SUN

FROM THE EARTH, the moon appears to be about the same size as the sun. Actually, the sun is about 400 times as large in diameter as the moon, but it also happens to be about 400 times as far away, so that the two objects look the same size in the sky. When the moon passes in front of the sun, it can completely cover the sun. Then a total eclipse of the sun takes place.

An eclipse does not occur each time the moon goes around, because of the slight inclination of the moon's orbit. Normally, the new moon passes a little above the sun or a little below it, and no eclipse takes place. At least twice and as often as five times a year, however, it passes in front of the sun, so that there are from two to five eclipses of the sun each year.

Not all of these eclipses will be alike, nor will an eclipse appear the same from all parts of the earth. At some locations, the moon may cover only a part of the sun, and there it is a partial eclipse. At times, the moon does not appear large enough to cover the whole sun. The distance from the earth to the moon averages about 239,000 miles, but the moon's orbit around the earth is elliptical. It can be as close to the earth as 221,000 miles, or as far away as 253,000 miles. When it is farther away, it looks smaller, and even though it passes directly in front of the sun, a thin ring of sunlight remains visible around the moon. Then the eclipse is *annular*.

A total eclipse of the sun occurs only when the moon passes directly in front of the sun and is close enough to the earth to cover the sun completely. This is by far the most interesting kind of eclipse. It begins as a partial eclipse. As the moon slowly covers it, the sun becomes a smaller and smaller crescent of brightness. It takes about an hour to cover the sun completely, and in the last few minutes, the sky and earth begin to darken noticeably. Strange shadows race across the ground. Nature seems hushed and waiting. Then the sun is completely covered and one of the most awesome and beautiful sights in the heavens suddenly becomes visible.

Photos: American Museum-Hayden Planetarium

THE LONG ECLIPSE OF 1955

DURING A TOTAL ECLIPSE, the sun is covered for a short time; the longest possible is only 7½ minutes. Within that time, as the new moon completely covers the bright face of the sun, other parts of the sun, normally hidden in the brightness of daytime, are visible. The thin ring of the chromosphere and the pearly-gray light of the corona, parts of the sun's atmosphere, shine out like a halo around the moon. Brilliant scarlet prominences stand like tongues of flame on the edge of the sun. In the few seconds or minutes that these phenomena are visible, astronomers must work swiftly to investigate them.

Although total eclipses occur nearly every year, they are visible from only a small part of the earth's surface. Often this small region is situated over an ocean or is otherwise inaccessible, or is noted for poor weather. Some of the eclipses last but a few seconds. During an astronomer's lifetime, he can look forward to very few minutes of observing these interesting and important features of the sun, and he could lose many of these few moments if one stray cloud wanders across the sun at the wrong moment.

That is why so many astronomers were anxious to observe the total solar eclipse of June 30, 1955, the longest eclipse in over 1,200 years. The eclipse was visible only from Ceylon, Burma, Thailand, French Indo-China, and the Philippine Islands; the rest of its path was over water. Chances for good weather were best in Ceylon, so astronomers from all over the world gathered there. Some had come six months in advance to set up and test their complex equipment. The length of this eclipse was so attractive that they were willing to risk the expense and time in traveling great distances and transporting tons of equipment.

On the morning of June 30, on Ceylon, hundreds of astronomers and millions of curious natives waited for the skies to clear, but they never did. The eclipse came and went behind clouds so dense that no records of any importance were obtained. Every story of science cannot end in success.

Photos, map: American Museum-Hayden Planetarium
(upper photo): Swiss team at Polonnaruwa, Ceylon
(lower photo): Harvard astronomers at Sigiriya, Ceylon

THE LONG ECLIPSE OF 1955

TOTAL SOLAR ECLIPSE — JUNE 20, 1955

OBSERVER'S VIEW
ALONG PATH OF
TOTAL ECLIPSE

A TRIP TO THE MOON

THE MOON has always been a challenge to men. All sorts of plans and schemes have been devised for journeying to it. Many of the plans have come from the imagination of fiction writers; most of them are impossible. Now serious men of science are working on the problems that must be solved to make the trip a reality. Modern rocket engines can drive a ship through space even better than through the air. As these engines develop in power and efficiency, with better fuels and better ships to drive, a trip to the moon will not only be possible, it will be made.

The moon would be an ideal place for an astronomical observatory, free from the obscuring effects of the earth's atmosphere. More could be learned about the earth, its weather, and the ways in which the sun affects weather. Mineral experts would study the moon's rocks and mountains. Puzzling questions about the moon itself would be answered. Eventually men might use the moon as the jumping-off station for trips to other planets.

Of course, the trip cannot yet be made. We still do not understand fully the perils of traveling through space. It may be necessary first to establish a giant artificial moon or satellite a thousand miles or so above the earth, from which to launch the moon rocket. Even if a space ship did get to the moon, there would be enormous difficulties in landing, moving around, constructing shelters, and just plain keeping alive. The moon is a world without air, water, plants, animals, or supplies. It is terribly hot by day and intensely cold at night.

Space-flight experts know of these and other problems, and they are constantly at work trying to find ways to overcome them. No one knows when the first lunar voyage will take place. It may come with the very slow and gradual improvement in the design and use of rocket engines and space ships. Or it may come suddenly, the result of a mighty pioneering effort. But there is no longer any doubt that men will make a trip to the moon.

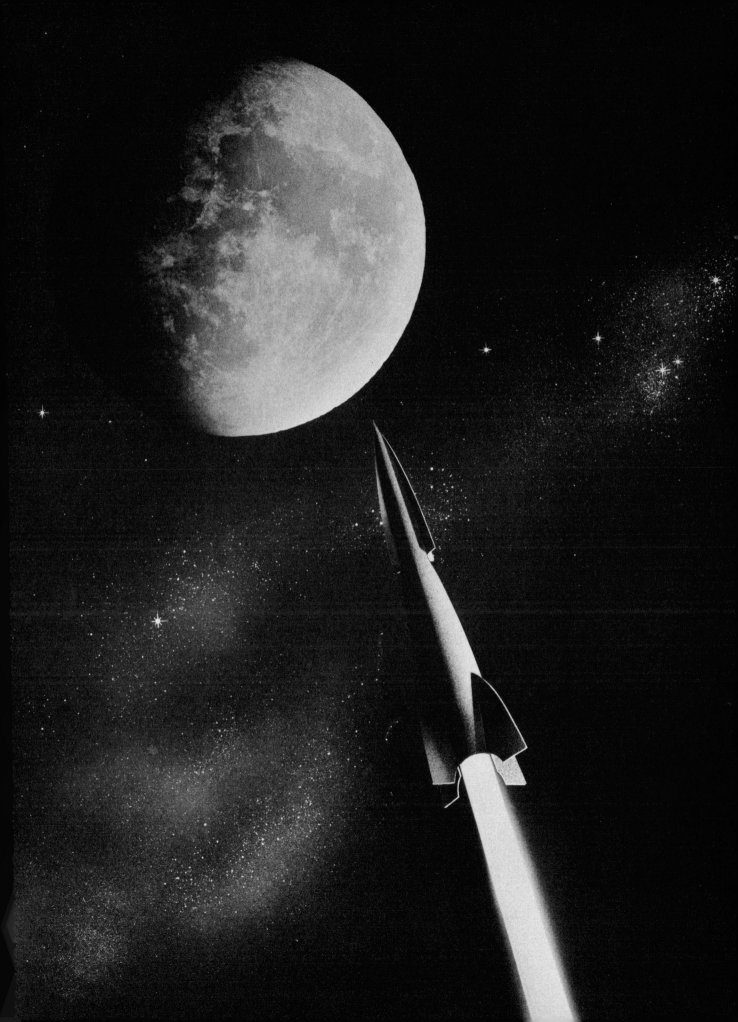

CHAPTER IV

THE SOLAR SYSTEM

ALL OF THE EARTH's nearest neighbors in space are members of a complicated family known as the solar system—the family of the sun. The members include a great many different objects. There is one star—the sun, described in another chapter. There are nine planets, of which the earth is one, thirty-one known satellites, thousands of asteroids and comets, and billions of meteoric particles.

In spite of their numbers and the tremendous mass these objects represent, more than 99 percent of all their material is concentrated in the sun. The enormous mass of the sun, through the gravitational force it exerts, controls the positions and movements of every member of the solar system.

THE SUN'S FAMILY

ONE OF THE MOST FASCINATING FEATURES of the solar system is that it seems well-ordered and regular in its motions. Imagine that you are an observer far out in space looking down over the north poles of the sun and earth. You would be impressed with the size and brightness of the sun as compared to the relatively insignificant planet members of its family. In fact you would do well to see the planets at all.

But look closely. Little Mercury can be seen hustling around the sun. Venus is next and then earth, each moving more slowly than the one before. The sun's gravitational attraction is controlling them, and the nearer the sun, the faster the motion necessary to counter this great force.

We notice, too, that all the planets move in the same direction, counter-clockwise from our vantage point over the north poles. If we were to watch from space beyond the south poles, the direction of motion would be clockwise. Some of the planets have satellites, and we observe that most of them are moving in the same direction around the planets that control them. A close look at the planets themselves, and the sun, reveals that they are turning around on their axes, also the same way, though here there is one exception (Uranus), and there are some uncertainties (Venus and Pluto).

Now let us change our imaginary spot in space and move to a new location away from the sun in the direction of the earth. If we were far out beyond the planets and looking back toward the sun, we would find another puzzling regularity: all of the planets except Pluto move not only in the same direction, but very nearly in the same plane that the earth's motion around the sun describes. Indeed, the planets' orbit planes very nearly coincide with each other.

In the picture, the planets are shown in relative size, in the order of their distance from the sun—Mercury, Venus, Earth, Mars, Jupiter, Saturn, Uranus, Neptune, and Pluto. To the right the number of known satellites is shown for each planet. Scale of size for the satellites is some-what distorted.

MERCURY

MERCURY was the messenger of the gods in the days of mythology. He is usually pictured as a healthy young fellow with winged feet who travels rapidly from place to place. His planet namesake is appropriately labeled, for this moon-like object so close to the sun revolves at an average speed of about 30 miles per second and occasionally moves as fast as 36 miles per second. This makes it the speediest of all the regular members of the solar system, completing a trip around the sun once each eighty-eight earth days.

Mercury is like the moon for several reasons. It has a low surface gravity and is therefore unable to retain an atmosphere of fast-moving gases. It is a dry, unchanging little world, for without air there is no sound, no rain, snow or clouds, and no erosion. Most important, tidal forces cause it to keep the same side toward the object around which it is moving—the sun. That side is therefore extremely hot, so hot that tin and lead would be liquid. On the other side, which never receives light and heat from the sun, temperatures plunge down to nearly —459° F. (absolute zero). This makes Mercury the planet of greatest heat and cold.

The orbit of this planet is more elliptical than any other, except distant Pluto. As a result, it is sometimes considerably closer to the sun than at other times, and the variations in speed of revolution are large. Yet it is always so close to the sun that it is seen from the earth only with difficulty, and, from middle latitudes, is never seen more than two hours after sunset or more than two hours before sunrise.

Occasionally, Mercury can be observed as a small black dot in transit across the sun. This occurs when it is directly between earth and sun, most recently on November 14, 1953 and May 5-6, 1957. A transit will take place again on November 7, 1960.

No photograph of Mercury is available which clearly shows its surface features. The illustration was painted from the sketches and accounts of many observers.

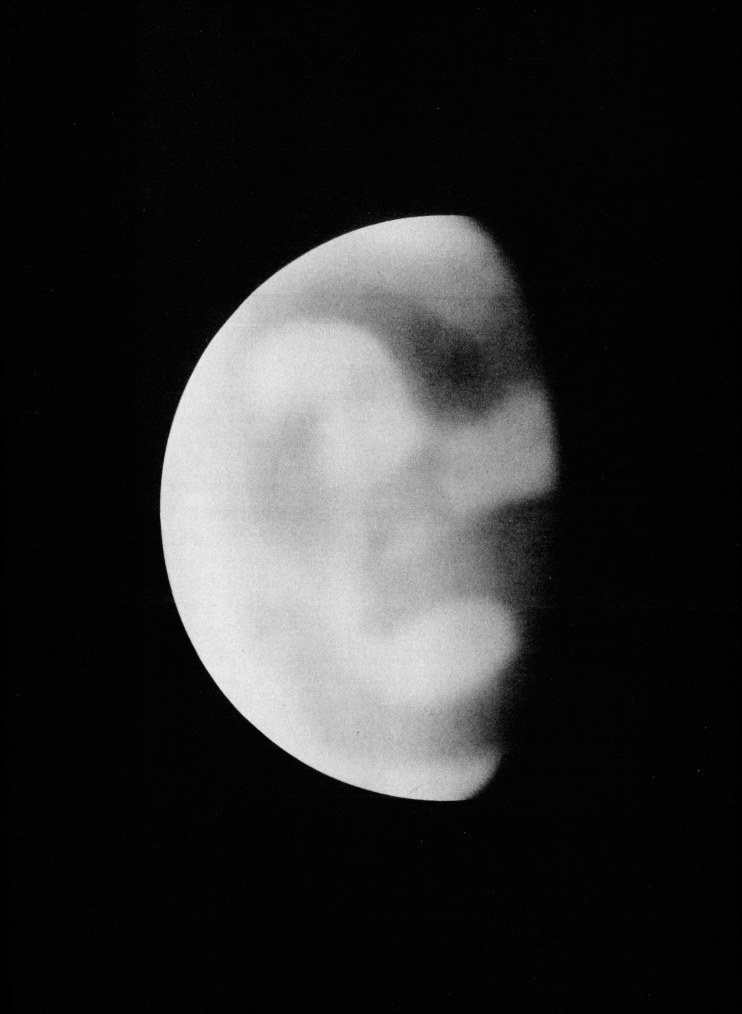

VENUS

VENUS is our closest planet neighbor. Once in every 19 months it comes within about twenty-six million miles of the earth. Only the moon, among the regular wanderers of space, comes closer. Yet, when Venus is close to us, it is between earth and sun, and we must look into the daytime sky at its dark side. Certainly this is not a good time for observation. Nevertheless, there are times when Venus becomes conspicuous. It can outshine every object in the sky except the sun and moon and can occasionally be seen in the daytime. Its varying appearance as it circles the sun is illustrated here.

In spite of its nearness and its brightness, Venus is often referred to as the "world of mystery." It is covered with a layer of clouds so dense that surface features have not been seen. Pictures taken of the planet recently with light of various colors, seem to reveal a few markings. They are so obscure, however, that they can only suggest whether the planet is turning on its axis. It is believed that it does—though the period is most uncertain. One recent investigation suggests a period of 225 days. If so, it is like Mercury with one side always directed toward the sun, for Venus' period of revolution around the sun is also 225 days. It is somewhat early to judge this new figure for rotation; most astronomers believe that a few weeks is a better estimate.

The composition of the clouds is also a mystery. The spectroscope discloses the presence of large amounts of carbon dioxide. An analysis of light reflection indicates that there might be water droplets or water vapor. This has been disputed, however, and many insist that Venus is a dry world.

A creature living at the surface of Venus would probably never see the stars, nor would he see the sun or other planets. He might be aware that one part of his world was dark and the other side very bright and hot, but he would not see the sun that was causing this condition. While Venus is a world of mystery to us, all the universe would be a mystery for someone confined to the surface of Venus.

Photo: Adapted from photographs by E. C. Sliphor, Lowell Observatory

EARTH

THE THIRD PLANET in order of distance from the sun is the only one which we know to be inhabited. In fact, life of all kinds abounds—animals, plants of endless variety, fishes and other marine creatures, and *people*. It is our earth. In no other part of the solar system, nor in any other part of the universe of which we have knowledge, is there a combination of surface features, air, and solar energy to which the existence of our kind of life is so perfectly suited. True, there may be a world somewhat like our own attending some distant star or stars, but even if there is, the vastness of space will no doubt serve as an effective barrier to our ever learning about it.

The earth is an interesting planet for several reasons. It has been discussed in detail in Chapter I, but we often overlook some of the important points simply because we are confined to its surface. For example, the earth and moon are more nearly the same size than any other planet and satellite combination. From Mars or Jupiter we would be considered twin planets. The earth is much brighter, though, reflecting perhaps one hundred times as much light as the moon.

The earth is the densest planet (possibly excepting Pluto), weighing five and one-half times as much as the same volume of water. Venus comes nearer than any other to having such density: 4.9 times that of water. At the other extreme is Saturn, which weighs only 0.7 as much as an equal volume of water; so little, in fact, that an average chunk of it could float in an earth ocean.

Perhaps the most surprising feature of Earth is its comparatively small size. Jupiter has a diameter eleven times as great, and a volume more than 1,300 times our own; the sun is much larger and even more massive. In spite of its many millions of tons of material, the earth is but an astronomical speck in the sun's domain of space.

Photo: American Museum-Hayden Planetarium

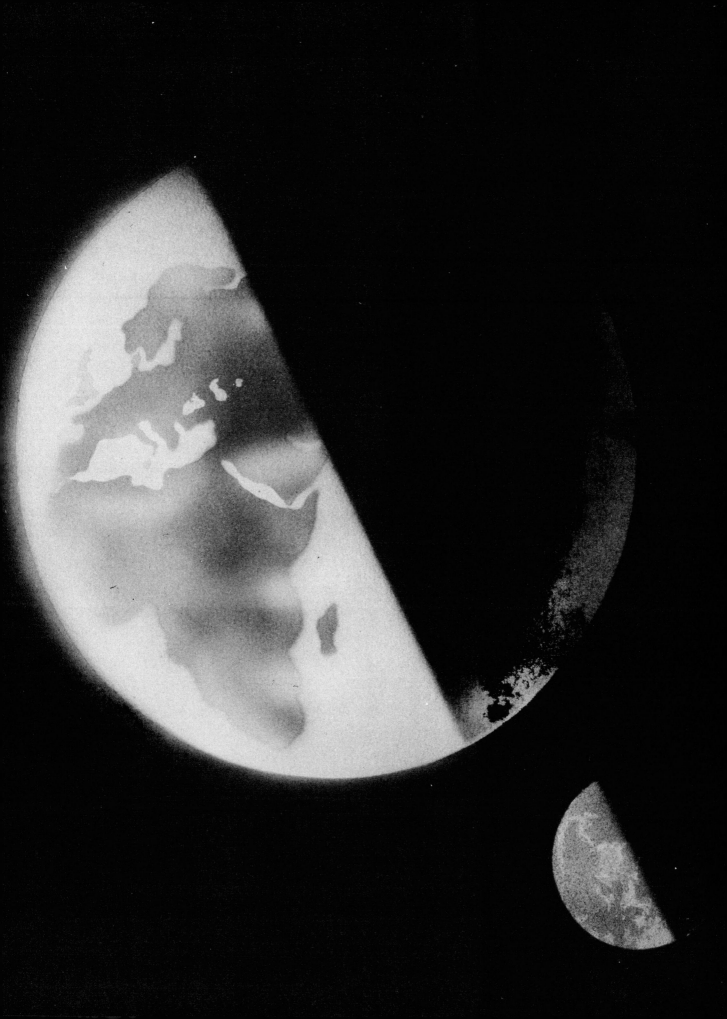

MARS

SINCE THE DAWN of civilization, people on the earth have looked into the night sky and have speculated about the strange reddish-hued world that occasionally reaches such brightness that it outshines all the stars. Because of its color it was named for the god of war, Mars.

Probably we know more about this little planet than any other. Though it does not come quite as close as Venus, it always presents to us a lighted side. Unlike Venus, our near neighbor in the sun's direction, we can study Mars carefully through many hours of the night. It has distinctive surface features; many of them have been charted and named. The darker regions are known as "seas," though they are not seas of water. The brighter regions, the copper-colored "continents," have been assigned names from mythology and from some geographical areas of the earth. There are polar caps, for Mars is tilted to the sun at an angle of 25° and has seasons that are similar to those on earth. In the Martian springtime the polar caps fade and something—perhaps water from melting ice—initiates a change in color in the nearby land.

In their search for life beyond the earth, scientists think that Mars is the most likely planet of any of those in the solar system. Yet its atmosphere seems to indicate that any life that does exist may be very different from our own. Only carbon dioxide has been certainly identified and there is but meager evidence of oxygen or water vapor. Our best guess is that the Martian air is composed mostly of nitrogen with a small percentage of carbon dioxide.

We still need to know much more about this planet before we can point rockets of the future to it and make a trip with some assurance that we shall be able to return. Investigation has been aided by the recent "favorable oppositions" of 1954 and 1956, when Mars came to within about 35,000,000 miles of the earth. An even better opposition will take place in 1971, when some of the many remaining questions about our rust-colored space neighbor may be resolved.

Photo: G. Kuiper, McDonald Observatory

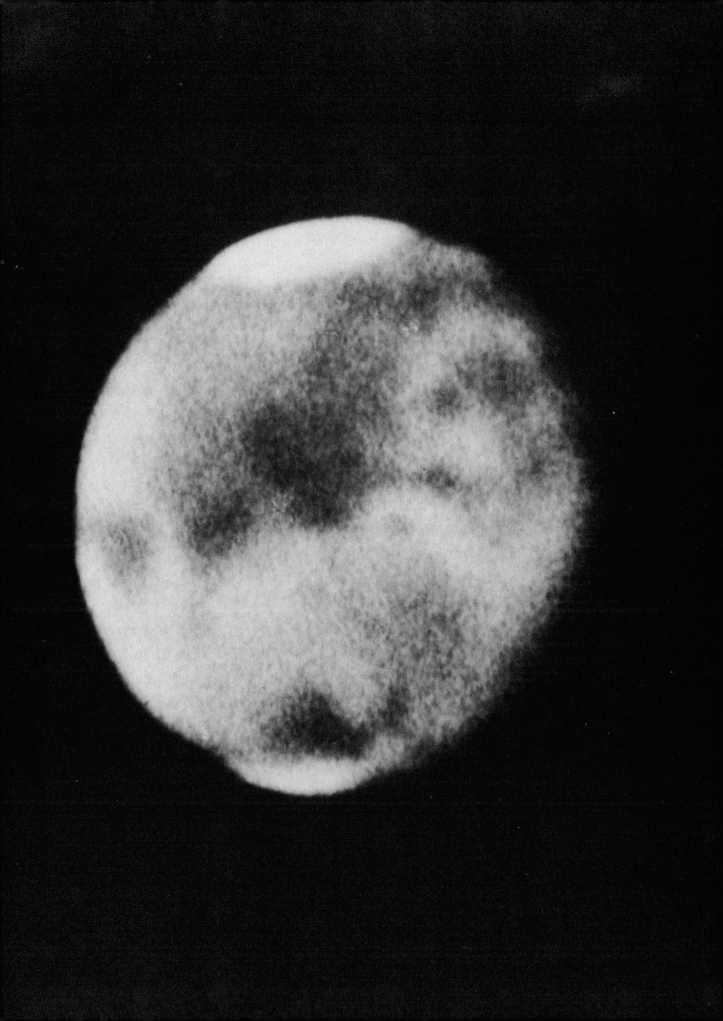

PHOBOS AND DEIMOS,
THE MOONS OF MARS

THE TWO SATELLITES of Mars are so small that they might well be considered mountains in space rather than full-fledged worlds. They were discovered by Professor Asaph Hall at the United States Naval Observatory during the favorable opposition of Mars in 1877.

Phobos, the nearer of the two to the planet, is probably not more than ten miles in diameter, yet it would appear to an observer on the Martian surface as the largest and brightest object in the sky except, of course, the sun. Only some 3,700 miles from Mars' surface, it would move frequently through the planet's shadow and be eclipsed from view.

Because it is so near the surface of Mars, where gravitational attraction is strong, Phobos must move at an extremely high speed to remain in its orbit. As a consequence, it revolves completely every 7 hours 39 minutes, only about one-third of a Martian day. Since this is faster than Mars rotates on its axis, the little moon would appear to rise in the west and set in the east, contrary to the motions of all other regular objects in the sky. It would be above the horizon for only about three hours, but during this time would go through about half of a full cycle of phases. From the poles, it would be perpetually hidden from view by the curvature of the Martian surface.

Deimos, averaging 12,500 miles from the surface of Mars, is not quite so spectacular. It is smaller than Phobos, likely no more than six miles in diameter. From Mars it would compare in brightness to some of the more easily-seen stars. It requires about 30 hours for a complete revolution, which is but a few hours more than a Martian day of 24 hours 37 minutes. Deimos would therefore be visible above a point on the planet's surface for nearly three days, but still going through its phases each revolution (though it might be difficult to see them).

Mars from Deimos, by Howard Russell Butler
Photo: American Museum-Hayden Planetarium

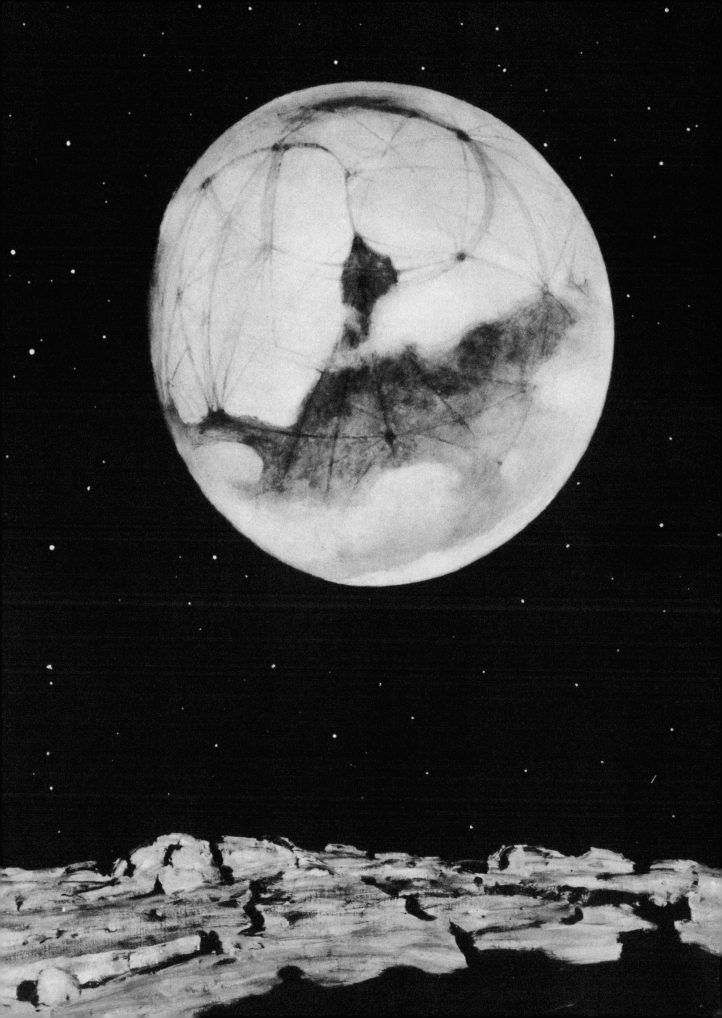

THE MINOR PLANETS

IN THE YEAR 1772, the German astronomer Johann Bode wrote about the curious mathematical relationship of the distances between planets. His *Bode's Law* has several faults, and cannot be used to determine accurately the distances between objects in the solar system. Nevertheless, in Bode's time, the "law" seemed to prove that there should be a planet between Mars and Jupiter, and many observers tried to find it. On January 1, 1801, the director of the Palermo Observatory, Giuseppe Piazzi, found a faint star-like object wandering slowly among the background of stars. The "wandering" proved that it was a member of the solar system, and continued observation demonstrated that it was a planet—not a comet as some had suggested.

Ceres, as the new object was named, is only 480 miles in diameter, hardly worthy of the label "planet." It has been referred to as a minor planet, or planetoid, or planetesimal. In 1802, a second minor planet 300 miles in diameter was discovered and it was named Pallas. Within a few years, Juno and Vesta were added to the list, and the new name of *asteroid* was suggested. Up to the present, more than 2,000 of these objects have been detected between Mars and Jupiter, and more are being found each year. They are assigned numbers in the order of their discovery, in addition to their mythological names. In recent years, discoveries have been so numerous that most any appropriate name has been used. For example, number 1230 is Riceia, named for Dr. H. S. Rice* of the American Museum-Hayden Planetarium staff.

Most of the asteroids are small; none is larger than Ceres. In the picture on the opposite page, Hermes is compared to the Island of Manhattan. Their orbits are often highly irregular, some of them revolving inside the orbit of Mars, others beyond Jupiter. In 1931, Eros was only 17 million miles from the earth, and was used to make measurements that have since improved the distance scale for the whole solar system.

---

*See the Foreword to this book.

Photo: American Museum-Hayden Planetarium

JUPITER

IN AN ORBIT slightly more than 500 million miles from the sun, the giant planet Jupiter revolves majestically once every twelve years. With a diameter of 88,000 miles and a retinue of twelve known satellites, it is the undisputed colossus of the sun's planet family. Its volume is more than 1,300 times, and its mass 318 times that of the earth. Gravitational attraction for nearby asteroids is so great that even the sun's control of them is at times temporarily disputed.

Pictures of Jupiter taken several weeks apart show that changes are constantly taking place in the surface features. The typical golden-brown hue is modified by several bands of varying form and color, spread parallel to the equator. Occasionally a drastic change occurs, such as the sudden appearance of the Great Red Spot in 1878. Though it had been seen before, something happened in that year to make the huge surface marking in the southern hemisphere more prominent. It has been fading since, but is still observable.

Many of the markings, like the Great Red Spot, are semi-permanent, permitting a determination of the period of rotation. At the equator, Jupiter rotates in a period of 9 hours 50 minutes, indicating that the material near the Jovian equator is moving around the axis at speeds very much greater than that of the earth's equatorial region. This is no doubt responsible for the color bands and also results in the noticeable flattening of the planet which can be seen in even a casual glance through a telescope.

The spectroscope reveals the presence of methane and ammonia. Methane, or "fire-damp," is the major component of some natural gas used in cooking and heating; ammonia's familiar odor is known to all housewives who use the material for cleaning. Neither is pleasant to human beings, to say the least. A surface temperature of about $-200°$ F. suggests that part of the ammonia has frozen to form crystal clouds much like the high, cirrus ice clouds in our atmosphere. From these facts and others, we conclude that the surface of Jupiter that we see is the upper layer of clouds and gases in turbulent motion. Somewhere beneath there may be another—perhaps solid—surface, which has never been observed.

Photo: Yerkes Observatory

JUPITER'S ONE DOZEN MOONS

JUPITER possesses four satellites so large and bright that they could be seen without optical assistance if the light from the planet itself were not so brilliant. Ordinary binoculars or almost any telescope reveal them easily. It is not surprising that they were discovered by Galileo with his first telescope in 1610; they have been known ever since as the Galilean satellites.

The two largest, Ganymede and Callisto, are larger than the planet Mercury; Io is larger than the moon, Europa only slightly smaller. All are large enough to serve as respectable planets if they were in orbits around the sun rather than Jupiter. They revolve rapidly, the fastest in one day and eighteen hours, the slowest in sixteen days and seventeen hours. All are nearly in the plane of Jupiter's equator, sometimes crossing in front of the planet, at other times occulted behind it.

Almost three hundred years after the discovery of the Galilean satellites, others were seen for the first time. In 1892, Barnard identified an object nearer the planet than the known four. Within the next twenty-two years, four others were found. In 1938, two more were added to the list, and the most recent was reported in 1951. All of them are small, ranging in size from fifteen miles to one hundred miles in diameter. Curiously, no names have ever been adopted for them, and they are identified by Roman numerals assigned in order of their discovery. Thus Barnard's 1892 satellite is Jupiter V, and Nicholson's 1951 find is Jupiter XII.

Sometimes these small satellites are grouped according to their orbital characteristics. Satellites VI, VII, and X are about seven million miles from the planet on the average, and revolve in about 260 days. Satellites VIII, IX, XI, and XII are nearly fifteen million miles from Jupiter and require about 740 days for a complete revolution. Perhaps the strangest feature of these four outermost moons is that they travel opposite the direction of revolution of the other eight satellites, and for that matter, opposite in direction to most of the members of the solar system.

Jupiter from Io
Painting: American Museum-Hayden Planetarium

SATURN

JUPITER AND SATURN seem to have been created from the same batch and cast to the same mold. Most of what is said about the one applies with but a variation in degree to the other. In size, Saturn is second only to Jupiter, and with its equatorial diameter of 75,000 miles, it is still large enough to contain over 700 earths. Its rapid rotation period of ten hours fourteen minutes (some twenty-three minutes longer at the slower-moving poles) has bulged it out at the equator proportionately more than its titanic neighbor. Thus, the polar diameter of Saturn is only 67,000 miles, and the difference is easily detected in a small telescope.

Even the surface markings suggest similarity to Jupiter, and occasional large-scale disturbances have been recorded. The atmosphere that we view appears to be a more pacific, considerably colder version, but its features are sufficiently clear that the rotation period can be approximated. With a surface temperature of −240° F., most of the ammonia so prominent in the atmosphere of Jupiter has been frozen out, leaving methane as the material most easily identified.

Using information from observations, principles in physical dynamics, and some assumptions, Professor Rupert Wildt has devised a model of the possible structure of the giant planets. According to this scheme, Saturn has a rocky core of diameter 20,000 miles. Surrounding that is a layer of ice 15,000 miles thick, and then a solid hydrogen envelope about 12,000 miles thick. The methane and ammonia must exist in an atmosphere composed chiefly of hydrogen, and the rather uncertain distinction between the gas and the solid must depend heavily on the temperature. In other words, it seems unlikely that Saturn, or any of the other giant planets, has a definite surface like the earth and the other earth-like planets. Saturn appears to be another forbidding world, from the space visitor's point of view!

Photos: American Museum-Hayden Planetarium
Mt. Wilson and Palomar Observatories; 100-inch photograph

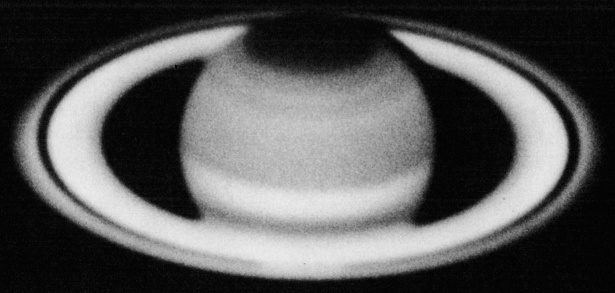

THE FABULOUS RINGS OF SATURN

ALTHOUGH SATURN IS NUMBERED among the major planets, and is like them in many respects, it has a unique system of rings that identify it unmistakably. Because of these rings, an observer looking through a telescope for the first time probably gets a greater thrill from a view of Saturn than from any other object in the skies. Galileo saw the rings in 1610, but he could not understand what they were, and probably believed that Saturn was a triple planet.

The rings go through a cycle of change each thirty years as the planet revolves, for the rings—like the planet's equator—are inclined to the ecliptic. At fifteen-year intervals, they are on edge as viewed from the earth. During the period between, more and more of the ring system can be observed; it is at its best about seven and one-half years after the edge-on position. The picture on the opposite page explains this cycle of change.

The rings measure 175,000 miles in outside diameter. There are three separate, distinct parts. The middle one, about 16,000 miles wide, is much the brightest. The outer ring has about half that width. Inside the other two is the crepe ring, about 10,000 miles wide, so transparent that the planet itself can be seen clearly through its murky form. It was not detected until 240 years after Galileo had seen the others for the first time.

There are several significant facts about the physical nature of this fabulous system. It is not a solid band. The spectroscope reveals with certainty that, in accordance with Kepler's Laws, the parts of the rings nearest the planet revolve more rapidly, while the distant parts revolve more slowly. Millions of small particles of rock or ice (or both), constrained to revolve in an orbit almost in the plane of the planet's equator, must constitute this planetary ring system.

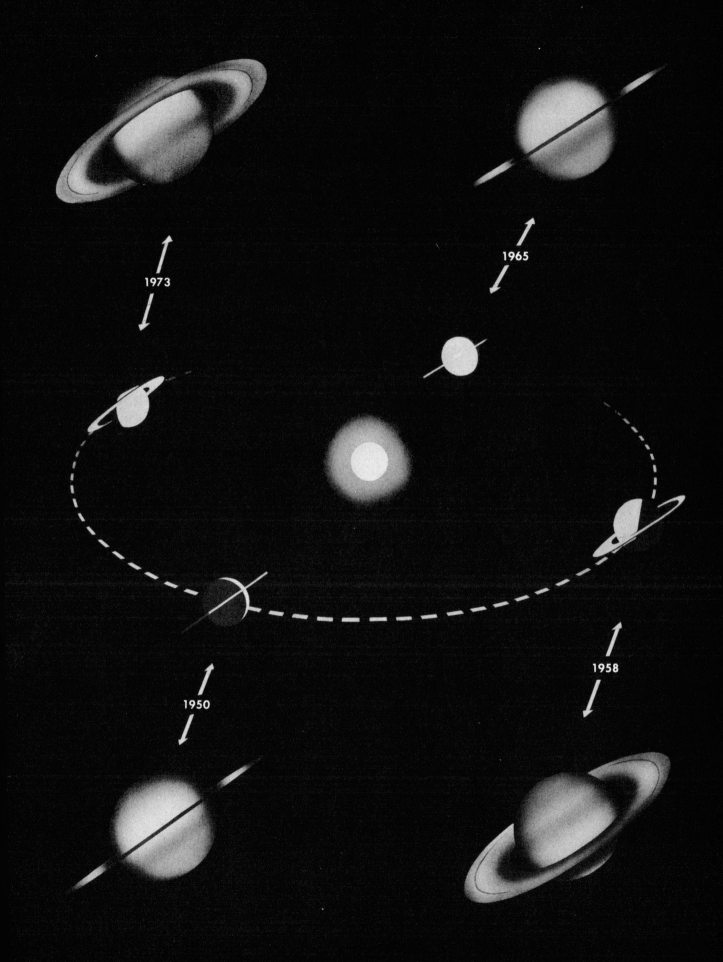

SATELLITES OF SATURN

LIKE JUPITER, Saturn has a large satellite family; it numbers nine members. Some facts about these objects are uncertain, for Saturn's great distance from the sun makes them difficult to study.

Titan is the largest moon. It is considerably larger than our moon, and is probably at least as large as Jupiter's largest attendants, Ganymede and Callisto. Some vague surface features have been seen clearly enough to suggest that the same side of Titan always faces Saturn, a condition that should be expected from a knowledge of tidal forces and a comparison with other satellites more easily observed. Perhaps the most interesting feature of Titan is that it has an atmosphere. Like that of its primary, Saturn, the principal constituent is methane, though the quantity is very small.

Within the orbit of Titan are the orbits of five other satellites: Mimas, Enceladus, Tethys, Dione, and Rhea. They range in diameter from 400 to about 1,100 miles, have a low density, and are probably composed of a mixture of rock and different kinds of ice.

Hyperion, with a diameter of about 300 miles, travels around Saturn in an orbit just beyond Titan's. In spite of its comparatively small size, it has been known since 1848. Beyond it lies Iapetus, which lays claim to a special distinction. Like Titan, and others of the Saturnian satellites, Iapetus probably keeps the same side to its primary. If it does, different parts of its surface are presented to us, and at times this little world appears five times brighter than on other occasions. We must conclude that the surface composition is remarkably varied.

The last of Saturn's system of known satellites is Phoebe. Like the outer satellites of Jupiter, Phoebe revolves in a retrograde manner. It is over eight million miles from Saturn and requires a year and one-half to complete one revolution.

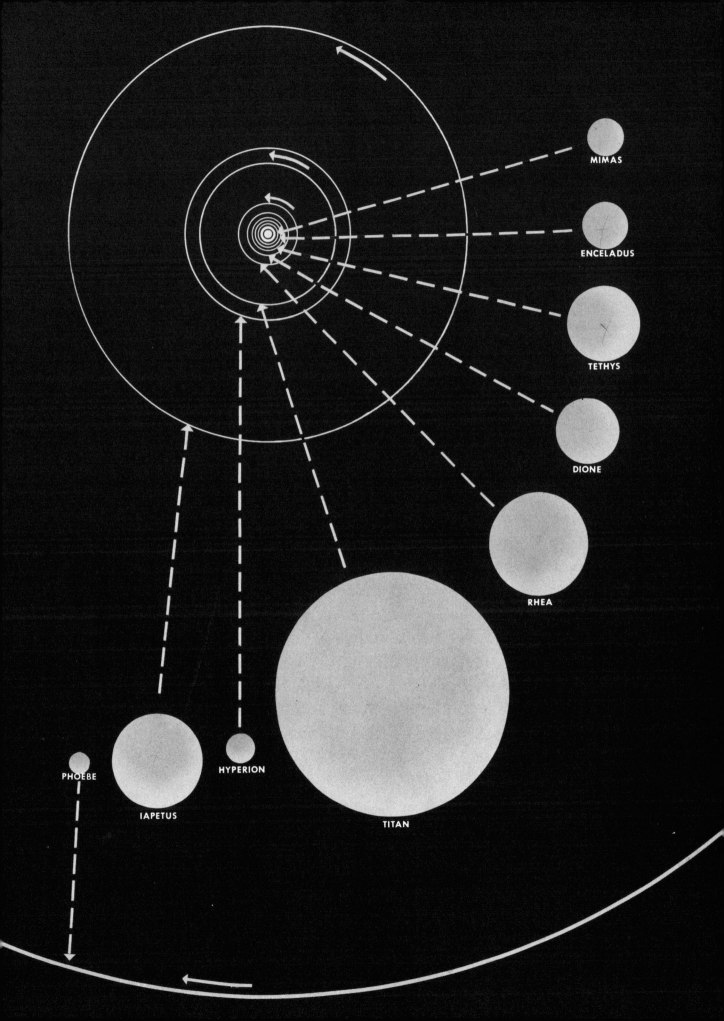

MIMAS

ENCELADUS

TETHYS

DIONE

RHEA

TITAN

HYPERION

IAPETUS

PHOEBE

URANUS AND NEPTUNE

URANUS AND NEPTUNE are usually listed with Jupiter and Saturn among the giant worlds. Uranus has a diameter of about 31,000 miles; Neptune is somewhat smaller and considerably more dense. Both probably have small rocky cores surrounded by ice and solid hydrogen, and possess atmospheres that exhibit clear evidence of methane. At their extremely low surface temperatures, it is likely that ammonia—such an important part of the atmospheres of other major planets—has been completely frozen out. A few surface markings can be detected, but they are quite indistinct; through a telescope, both planets appear as greenish disks.

William Herschel discovered Uranus in 1781. Actually it had been plotted on previous star maps, though its true nature had not been suspected. In the few decades following its discovery, Uranus seemed to defy the rules. By 1845, the actual position as it was seen in the sky and the positions calculated by the mathematicians were greatly different.

There was a possible explanation. If another planet were located beyond Uranus, then according to the laws of gravitation, that other planet would affect the motions and position of Uranus. By comparing the difference between the predicted and actual motions it was possible to estimate the mass and approximate location of the disturbing object. Searching the heavens at a point where mathematicians had predicted that another planet would be found, Galle, at Berlin, on the night of September 23, 1845, discovered the new planet. It was named Neptune.

Uranus has five satellites, all of which are visible in this picture. Herschel himself discovered two of them, Titania (far right) and Oberon (upper left). Two more were found in 1851. They have been labeled Ariel (below left of Uranus) and Umbriel. In 1948 the fifth one was seen for the first time by Kuiper at the McDonald Observatory in Texas and has been named Miranda. It can be seen as a minute dot inside the halation rings to the right of the planet.

Neptune has two satellites: Triton with a diameter of about 3,000 miles, and tiny Nereid, discovered by Kuiper in 1949.

Photographed with an 82-inch McDonald reflector
Photo: G. Kuiper, Yerkes Observatory

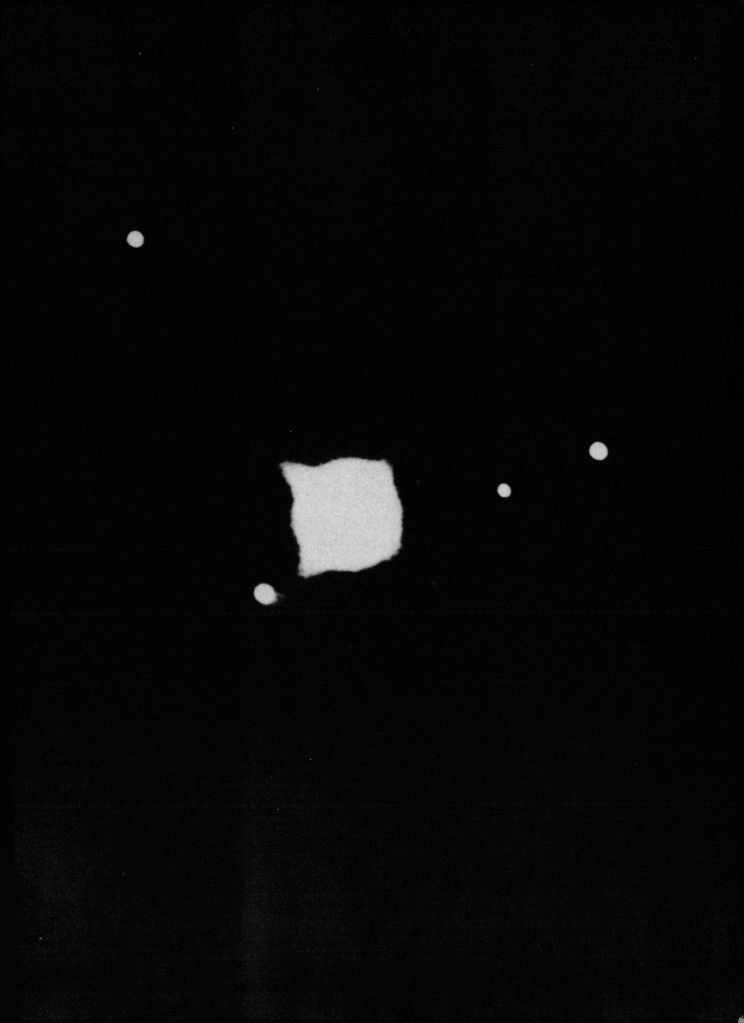

A STRANGE YEAR

FROM KEPLER'S THIRD LAW we learn that the more distant planets require more time to complete an orbit around the sun, and that the nearer planets revolve more rapidly. Thus, Mercury goes around once each 88 days, the earth, once each year, and Saturn, once each 29½ years. Uranus is at that distance which requires 84 years for such a cycle. To express it another way, a Uranian year is 84 earth years long. Like the other major planets, Uranus rotates rapidly, turning around on its axis once every 10¾ hours. This combination of rapid rotation and slow revolution results in a year of 68,506 days. For this reason alone, time on Uranus would be radically different from that to which we are accustomed.

But another factor must be added which complicates things even more. The axis of Uranus lies within eight degrees of the plane of the orbit, so that the poles, as well as the equator, will at some time be directed nearly toward the sun. There is no permanent torrid zone nor any permanent frigid regions (such things are comparative, of course; due to its great distance from the sun it is always cold on all parts of Uranus). Imagine a year 84 times longer than our own, with so many more days, and with the sun appearing at one time or another in almost any part of the sky!

One other feature of Uranus serves to confuse matters still further. The end of the axis which is above, i.e., north of the plane of the orbit, is the South Pole. This is the upper end of the axis in the picture. Or, if we choose to call this pole the North Pole, then we must admit that Uranus is rotating backwards, clockwise, looking down from this pole. Every other planet rotates counterclockwise as viewed from this direction. Not only does the sky picture change radically through the year, but the apparent motions of the firmament are backwards. It appears that any future visitor to Uranus will have to be a calendar and time expert!

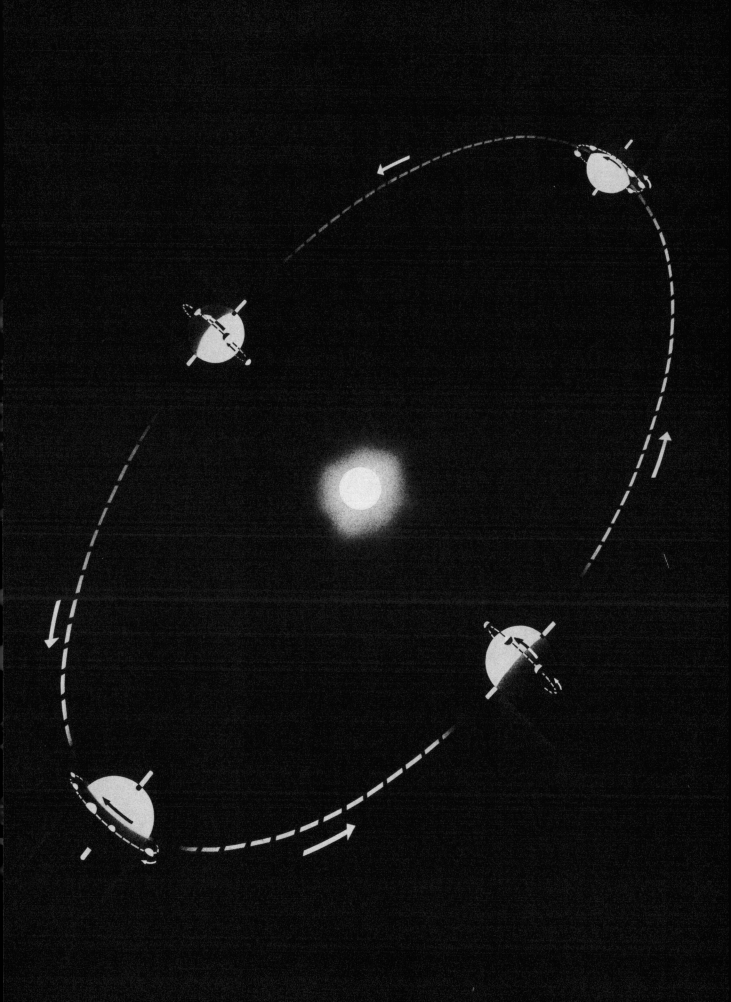

PLUTO

PLUTO, the most distant of the planets in the solar system, was discovered in 1930 by Clyde Tombaugh at the Lowell Observatory in Flagstaff, Arizona. It was detected on a photographic plate by means of the blink microscope, a laboratory instrument that identifies on a photo negative objects which are moving against the background of distant stars. Percival Lowell, the long-time director of the Observatory, must be credited with much of the perseverance and skill that led to the discovery. He had calculated the approximate position of "Planet X" using the unaccountable variations in the motions of Uranus and Neptune as guides. Unfortunately, Lowell did not live to see the successful outcome of his years of work.

Little is known of the physical nature of Pluto. We do know that it is so distant from the sun that it can receive very little heat energy. Surface temperatures must be within a few degrees of absolute zero ($-459°$ F.). Attempts have been made to determine the diameter, but due to the small amount of light, it is a difficult task. An attempt at such measurement in 1950 using the 200-inch telescope resulted in a value of 3,600 miles. If this is accurate, Pluto is more dense than the earth, and therefore quite unlike the other planets and satellites in the outer reaches of the solar system. These conclusions must be considered tentative. The period of rotation has been recently determined to be about six days and nine hours by photoelectric cell observations of the variation in its reflected light. The nature of the surface and other physical characteristics are unknown.

Because of an eccentric orbit and some similarity to Triton (Neptune's largest satellite), it has been suggested that Pluto was at one time a satellite that somehow escaped the gravitational control of its primary. Whatever it may once have been, it is now a planet, for Pluto's motions in its orbit are controlled primarily by the sun.

Two photographs of Pluto showing motion in twenty-four hours
Photos: courtesy Mt. Wilson and Palomar Observatories; 200-inch photograph

A STRANGE ORBIT

THERE ARE TIMES when Pluto is more than four and one-half billion miles from the sun. Yet, more than a century later, when it has traversed half of its orbit it is less than three billion miles from the sun—actually closer than Neptune! This variation in distance points up one of the most curious facts about Pluto's orbit—its great eccentricity, that is, the amount by which it departs from being a circle.

None of the planets travel around the sun in a perfect circle, though most come close to it. Venus and Neptune, for example, have orbits that are remarkably circular, while Mercury varies enough in its distance from the sun that the irregularity can be seen in a sketch of the path. None exhibits such tremendous differences as Pluto. It would almost seem to be an interloper that has somehow been caught up by the sun's gravitational greed, a sort of stranger in our midst.

In another respect Pluto's orbit is unlike that of the other planets. It is inclined to the earth's orbit plane by an angle of 17°, and is sometimes far above the plane described by the earth's motions, at other times millions of miles below it. All the other planets move around in orbits quite close to the plane of the earth's motion; even Mercury, other than Pluto the most errant, is in an orbit only 7° inclined.

The fact that Pluto is sometimes nearer the sun than Neptune has given rise to speculation about a possible collision between the two. Distance is not the only factor, however. Both planets would have to be in the same direction from the sun at the same time for such an event to occur. The inclination of the orbit and the differences in period of revolution around the sun make such a collision impossible.

COMETS

MOST COMETS, perhaps all of them, are permanent members of the solar system revolving in elliptical orbits around the sun. The orbits are highly eccentric, and a typical comet spends most of its time far from the sun, out beyond the orbits of Jupiter and Uranus, or even Pluto. When it does come close to the sun, internal changes occur which cause the comet to radiate energy of its own. Additionally, it reflects light from the sun, and through this combination can attain sufficient brightness to be seen by day. There are numerous comets recorded in astronomical history that were impressive, even frightening, to their observers. There are many others that can be seen only with a telescope, even at their brightest.

Comets have been referred to as "celestial gravel bags." They appear to be composed of numerous fragments of rock, dust, gas, and ice held loosely together. Recent theories propose that they may be composed mostly of different kinds of ice. A large part of the material of which they consist, whatever it may be, is concentrated in the *nucleus*. Surrounding this dense nucleus is the *coma,* a tenuous envelope from which most of the light is radiated and reflected. Streaming out from the denser parts in a direction opposite the sun is the comet's *tail*. The pressure of sunlight forces the tail to be so placed; it must be composed of very small fragments of matter. This matter originates in the nucleus and coma, and at each passage near the sun, the comet must expend some of its substance.

We may be living at a time when some bright comets have used so much of the available material that they can no longer be expected to shine as brightly as they once did. Perhaps many of the comets that have been recorded as objects of beauty and brightness will be seen no more. Others will probably take their place, however, and a bright new comet may appear at any time.

Morehouse's comet of 1908 is pictured here.

Photo: Yerkes Observatory

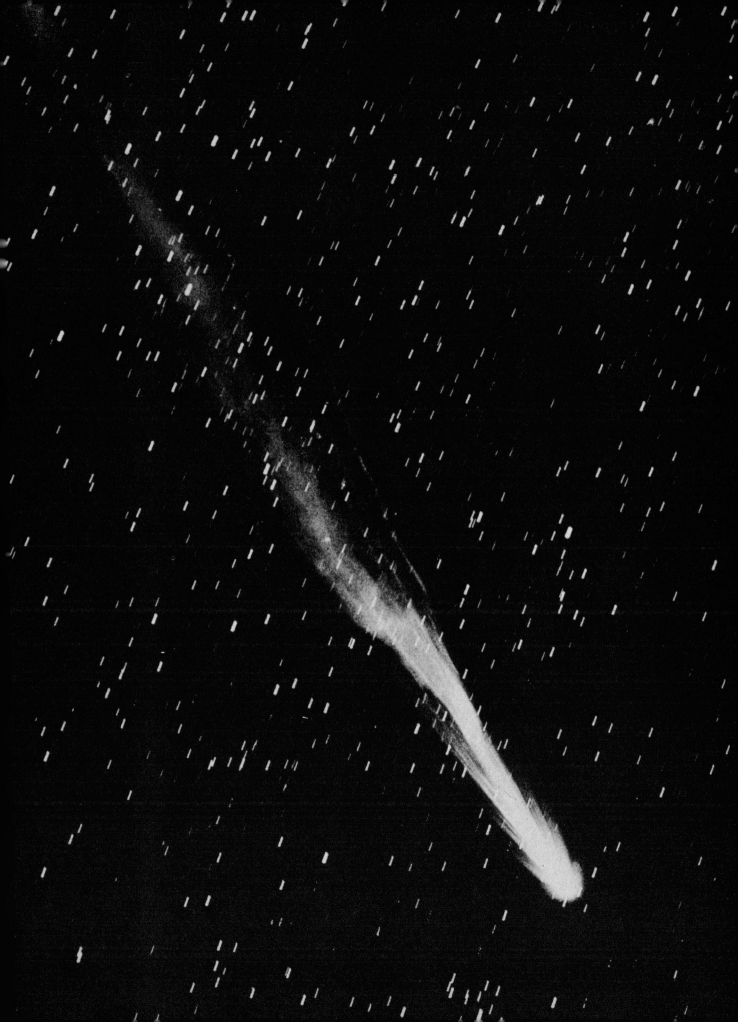

HALLEY'S COMET

ON MAY 20, 1910, a comet that had been clearly visible in the morning skies for about three weeks passed within fourteen million miles of the earth. It was so close that its tail swept through the atmosphere. Those who saw it attest to its being one of the most beautiful and awe-inspiring celestial sights they can recall. One observer writes that the "tail shone like a searchlight beam across the sky for 120°." To some, it was also a time of terror, for many people believed that there were poisonous gases in the tail that would kill everyone on earth, in spite of the assurances of astronomers that no harm could come.

Edmond Halley, at one time British astronomer royal, was the first to notice the repetitive nature of some comets. In particular, he noted that the comets of 1531, 1607, and 1682 were about 76 years apart, and after studying the orbits that had been recorded for each, concluded that it was the same comet returning at regular intervals. He predicted that it would return again in 1758 or 1759, and it did. It also appeared just about on schedule in 1835, and again—as we have noted—in 1910. Further research in old records—especially Chinese—resulted in the conclusion that Halley's Comet could be traced as far back as 240 B.C.

The problem of predicting the exact date of a comet's return is mathematically difficult. These objects have very little mass, perhaps less than one millionth that of the earth, and can be diverted greatly from their paths when they pass near one of the planets. The giant major planets—Jupiter, Saturn, Uranus, and Neptune—are especially troublesome in this respect. The prediction must therefore take into account the positions of each of the planets over a period of many years.

In 1950, Halley's Comet reached aphelion—its point of greatest distance from the sun. It is scheduled to return again to the vicinity of the earth and the sun in 1985 or 1986.

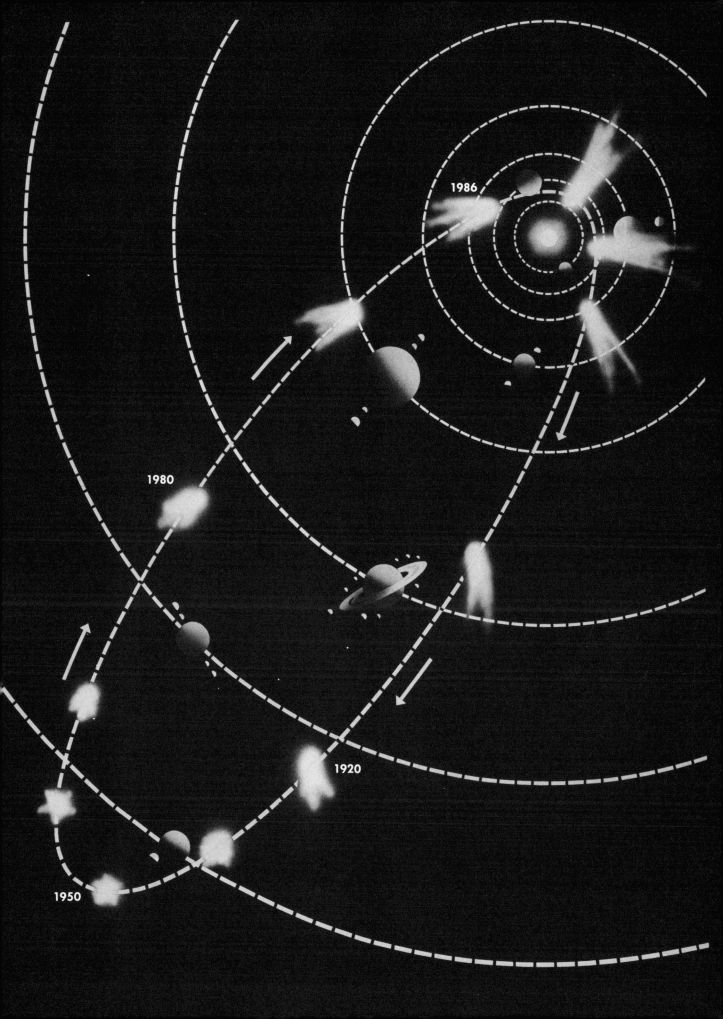

CHAPTER V

THE SUN

THE SUN is one of the most familiar objects in our everyday experience. We see it rise and set each day; we feel its warmth and see its light, and we are aware of how these change from season to season. Evidence of its influence is all around us, in the blue sky of day, the growth of trees and grass, the flow of rivers, and the winds that blow in the air.

All these, and many other features of our environment, are products of solar energy. Though some of these effects are obvious, the ways in which they are produced and the influence of slight variations in solar energy upon them are not well understood. The equally important effects of solar disturbances, occurring in cycles of activity, also require much further investigation.

Without doubt, the sun is the most important object of the heavens, in terms of its effect upon living things on earth. Ultimately, to know the earth better, it is necessary to understand the sun, its nature, activity, composition, physical processes, and the causes and effects of some of its features.

THE SUN IS A STAR

EVEN IN ANCIENT TIMES, the important role the sun played in sustaining life on earth was recognized. Quite obviously, it was something different from the earth itself. Its movements in the sky—rising and setting daily, and changing its path in the sky through a very regular cycle—were not understood. It was often considered, by primitive people and the earliest civilizations, as a god, whose wanderings in the sky reflected pleasure or displeasure with the ways of people on earth.

Today, we realize the influence and importance of the sun to an even greater degree than the ancients did. All of our energy sources—coal, oil, electricity, and water power—have come from the sun, directly or indirectly. We could not produce our food, and the rain on which we depend would not fall, without its light and heat. All of our weather, and the changing pattern of the weather which we struggle to understand, result from solar energy. Modern science, however, recognizes that the sun is not a mysterious, capricious deity, but a star—the nearest star to the earth—supporting life on earth through its normal star-like functions.

Seeing the stars only at night, and the sun only by day, some persons think of them as separate, unrelated kinds of objects. The sun is 93,000,000 miles from the earth on the average, quite some distance by our standards. But the next nearest star is about 25,000,000,000,000 miles away, over 270,000 times as far as the sun. Most stars we see at night are millions of times farther from us than the sun, so far that, though they are like the sun, and about the same order of size, they appear only as points of light—even in the greatest telescopes.

Astronomers, realizing the sun is a near-by star, have the opportunity of studying a star relatively close at hand. They can photograph it, study the appearance of its surface, and learn of the violent activity that goes on inside it and around it.

Photo: American Museum-Hayden Planetarium

THE NEAREST STAR

A CASUAL GLANCE at the sun shows that it is quite unlike the earth, so that we know stars must be different from planets. They differ in many ways. First, planets, like the earth, move around stars, like the sun. Secondly, stars are much larger than planets. They contain enormous amounts of material, many times more than the earth or even the largest planets. More important than that, however, stars and planets are constructed along entirely different lines.

Planets, as in the case of the earth, are solid or partly solid, cold and non-luminous. They receive light and heat from a nearby star. Ours come from the sun. Planets, therefore, might be considered as consumers or absorbers of light and heat.

On the other hand, the sun, like all stars, is made up entirely of gases at very high temperatures, and with tremendous pressure in the center. It is very brilliant and has its own internal source of energy which constantly supplies the light and heat it distributes into space. We might think of the sun as a manufacturer, supplier, and radiator of energy.

If you wanted to describe a typical star, you would do well to choose the sun as an example. It is a huge sphere of material, about 864,000 miles in diameter, maintained in a gaseous state by high temperatures. It would take 109 earths to cover a line across the center; 1,300,000 earths to fill up the space inside of it. If the earth were the size of a baseball, the sun would be as high as a three-story building.

Yet it is only a typical star, a little larger and brighter than most, but by no means the largest and brightest. The only thing special about the sun is its nearness to the earth. Its importance lies in its being the star that supplies us with light and heat.

(upper left): taken in hydrogen light   (lower left): ordinary light
(upper right): enlargement in hydrogen light   (lower right): in calcium light
Photos: courtesy Mt. Wilson and Palomar Observatories

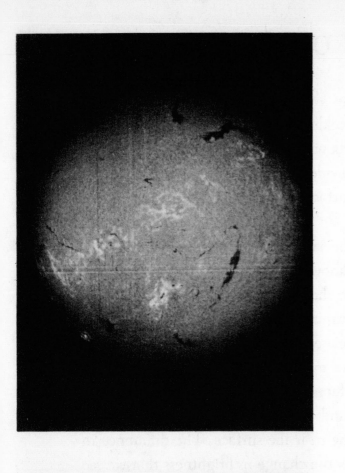

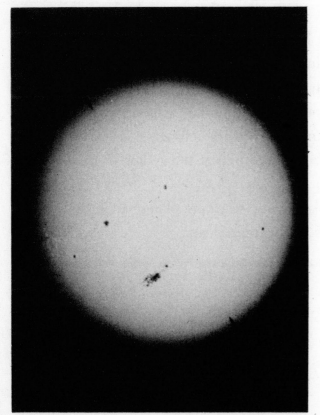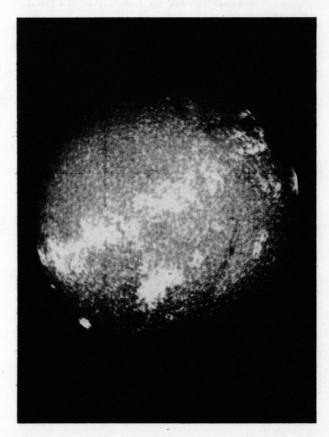

A PICTURE OF A STAR

PHOTOGRAPHS OF THE SUN show us the features of a typical star. The surface appears to be mottled or speckled, it does not seem to be evenly illuminated, and peculiar dark objects with very irregular shapes make an appearance from time to time. It is evident that the picture does not show the permanent markings of a solid surface. It does show the upper regions of a sphere of very hot gases.

The granulated appearance of the surface is real. The small, bright specks that produce the effect are known as granules. They are always present, but always different because they last for only a few minutes at most. As a result, the surface appearance is constantly changing. The enormity of the sun can be appreciated when it is realized that these granules are from 200 to 1,000 miles in diameter, yet there are from one to two million present on the sun's face at any one time. The granules are slightly brighter than the gases around them. They seem to be produced by currents of gas rising and settling near the surface. The difference in temperature of the currents produces the change in brightness that we see as the granules.

In the center the sun appears to be brightest. There is a very obvious darkening toward the edge, or limb, in all directions. The light at the center of the sun is coming on a direct path from the apparent surface. Near the edge, however, the light is coming from higher, cooler regions, and takes a longer path through the sun's atmosphere before we see it. It is less brilliant and slightly more yellow and red than at the center of the solar disk.

The very prominent dark areas are known as sunspots. These will be treated separately as one of the features of this typical star.

Photo: courtesy Mt. Wilson and Palomar Observatories

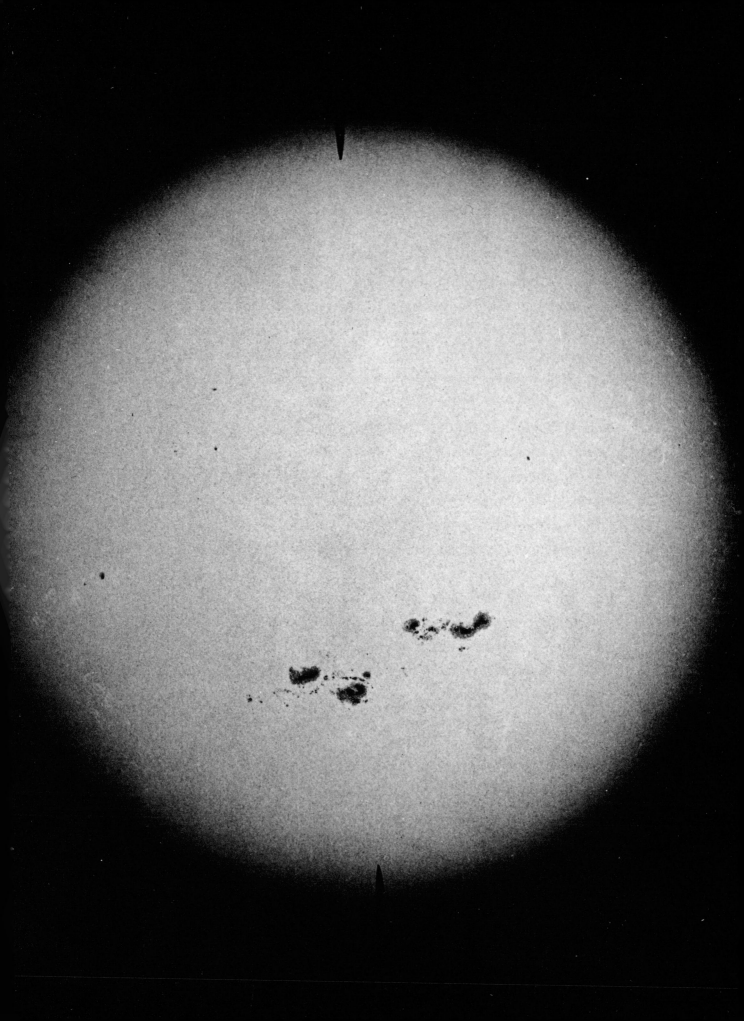

THE STRUCTURE OF THE SUN

THE INTENSE, BRILLIANT SURFACE of the sun, the bright, yellowish disk that we see, is known as the *photosphere* (meaning light-sphere). Beneath the photosphere is the interior of the sun, which cannot be seen or photographed and about which we can only speculate. It is supposed that it contains a central core, perhaps 200,000 miles in diameter, where most of the sun's energy is being produced. In this core, the temperature is thought to be above 20,000,000° C., and the material is packed together densely by pressure amounting to thousands of tons per square inch. Roughly 98 percent of the sun's light and heat originates from this central region and seeps out through a very deep, gradually thinning overlying layer. The top of that layer is the photosphere, where the temperature is much lower, about 6,000° C., and the pressure is less than one percent of atmospheric pressure at the earth's surface. Sunspots, and the minute granules, are seen on the surface of the photosphere.

Two other regions of the sun's atmosphere lie above the photosphere. Normally we cannot see them, because they are too faint against the illumination of the daytime sky. There is a thin, reddish layer, only a few thousand miles thick, known as the *chromosphere* (which means color sphere). The gases comprising it are very thin, less than a millionth of the atmospheric pressure at the earth's surface. It is from the chromosphere that the huge flame-like prominences, geysers of brilliant gas, are sometimes seen extending far above the sun's surface.

Above the chromosphere, there is a shell of very rarefied gas surrounding the sun, the *corona*. It is known to be many millions of miles thick, and its light is so faint that we cannot see it under normal conditions. Both the corona and the chromosphere are visible during a total eclipse of the sun. Astronomers can study them at other times with the aid of a special instrument called a coronagraph. This covers the bright photosphere and allows the fainter portions of the sun's atmosphere to be photographed.

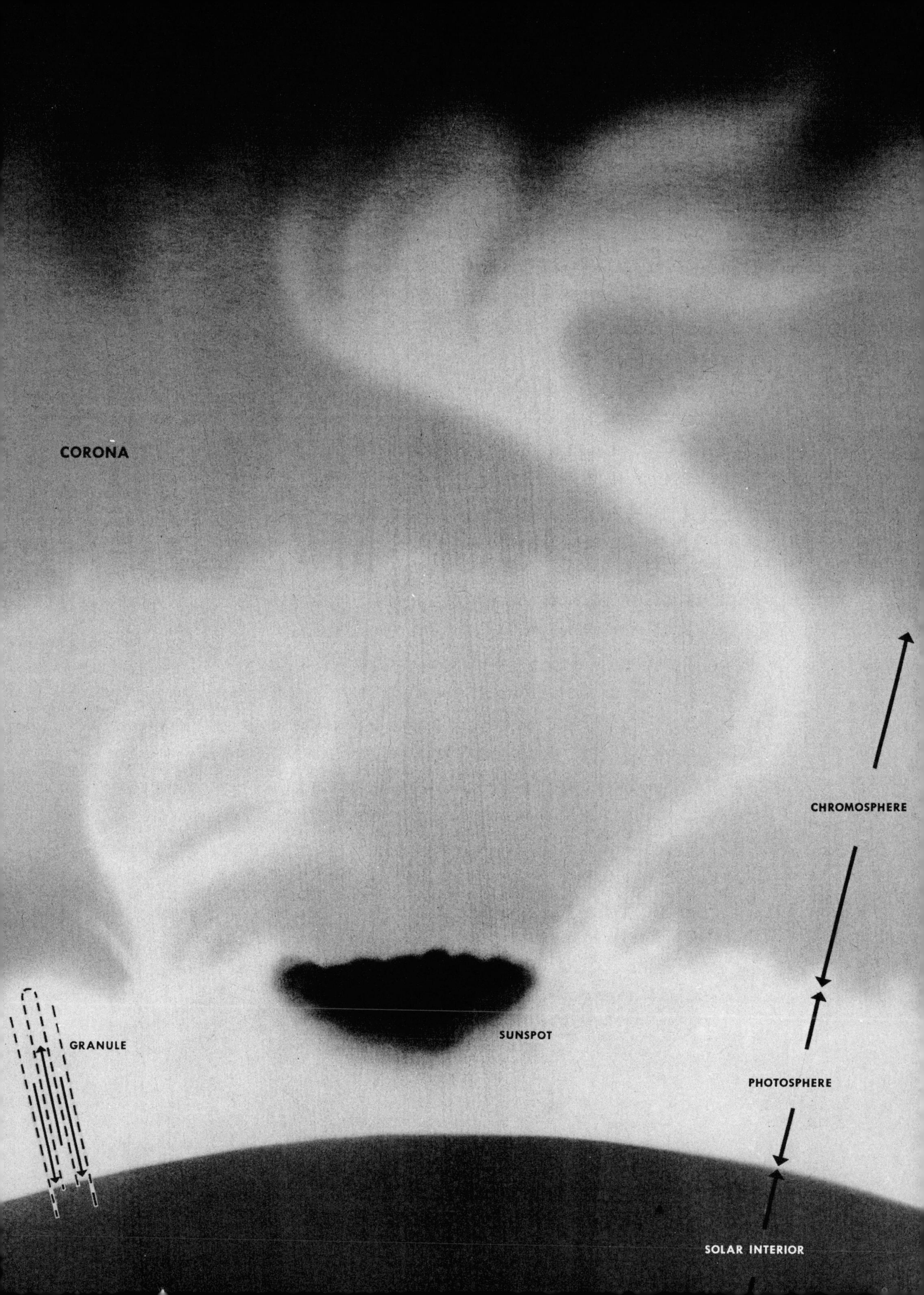

CORONA

CHROMOSPHERE

GRANULE

SUNSPOT

PHOTOSPHERE

SOLAR INTERIOR

THE SUN'S FINGERPRINTS

ALTHOUGH THE PHYSICAL CONDITIONS on the sun are entirely different from those on earth, the sun is made of the same material as that of the earth. Astronomers have been able to identify in the sun many of the basic chemical elements we know on earth. You might wonder how this could be possible, when the sun is 93,000,000 miles away. It became possible when a physicist named Fraunhofer discovered, in 1814, that sunlight contained "fingerprints."

The light coming from the dense, hot interior of the sun is almost pure white light, containing all the colors blended together. A prism would break up this light into a rainbow-like spectrum. Actually light behaves like waves of energy, with very definite wave-lengths. Each color is caused by waves with slightly different lengths. Light coming from the interior of the sun includes all wave-lengths, and hence all colors. A prism separates light according to the length of the waves in it, thus a prism separates it into its different colors. (See page 56.)

The light coming from the sun's interior must pass from the photosphere (the sun's surface) into the chromosphere, before we see it. The very rare gases at the bottom of the chromosphere, called the reversing layer, absorb some of that light. But each element can only absorb certain wave-lengths of light, so that the atoms of the various elements leave very thin, dark gaps in the colored spectrum of sunlight. When sunlight received on earth is directed through a prism, the spectrum always contains those dark lines. They are known as Fraunhofer lines, after their discoverer.

Astronomers have learned to identify the Fraunhofer lines with the chemical elements that cause them. In this way, they can determine what the sun is made of. To date, 66 of the 92 elements which occur naturally on earth have been identified in the sun.

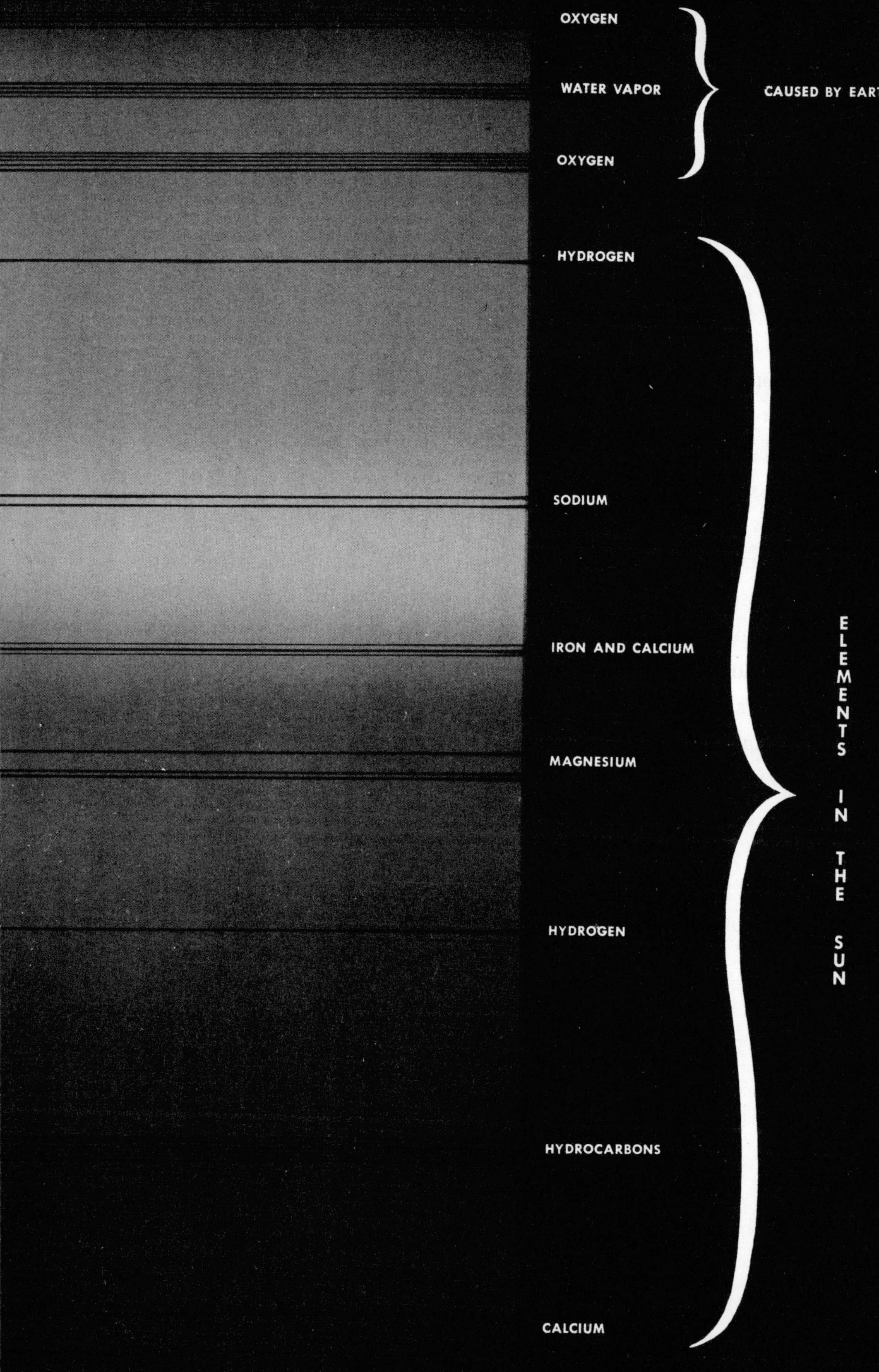

OXYGEN

WATER VAPOR   } CAUSED BY EART...

OXYGEN

HYDROGEN

SODIUM

IRON AND CALCIUM

MAGNESIUM

HYDROGEN

HYDROCARBONS

CALCIUM

ELEMENTS IN THE SUN

THE SUN'S ROTATION

AT CERTAIN TIMES, telescopic pictures of the sun show the dark markings which are called sunspots. When they are observed for several days, they are seen to drift across the visible face of the sun, always in the same direction. Large, prominent spots sometimes disappear on the west edge of the sun, and then reappear on the eastern edge several days later. It was recognized more than 300 years ago that this was evidence of the sun's rotation.

The sun rotates around an axis, but not quite like the earth. All places on earth rotate in the same period, once per day. But the sun is a gaseous sphere, not a solid body like the earth. Different zones of the sun rotate in different periods of time and more slowly toward each of its poles.

The motion of sunspots indicates that the sun rotates once in about 25 days at its equator. Halfway from the equator to the poles it takes about 28½ days. Close to the poles, the rotation takes place in a period of about 33 days. The direction of rotation is the same as the earth's, counterclockwise looking down at the north pole. The sun is much larger than the earth, so that its surface is moving more rapidly even though it takes much longer to complete a rotation. At the equator, it is traveling about 4,500 miles per hour even though it takes 25 days to go around once.

The sun's equator is inclined slightly to the plane of the earth's orbit, about 7°. In June and December, the north and south poles are on the edge of the sun as we see it. In March, the south pole of the sun is tilted slightly toward the earth, and in September, the north pole is tilted toward us.

*Successive photographs of the great sunspot of 1947, as it was
carried across the disk by the sun's rotation
Photo: courtesy Mt. Wilson and Palomar Observatories*

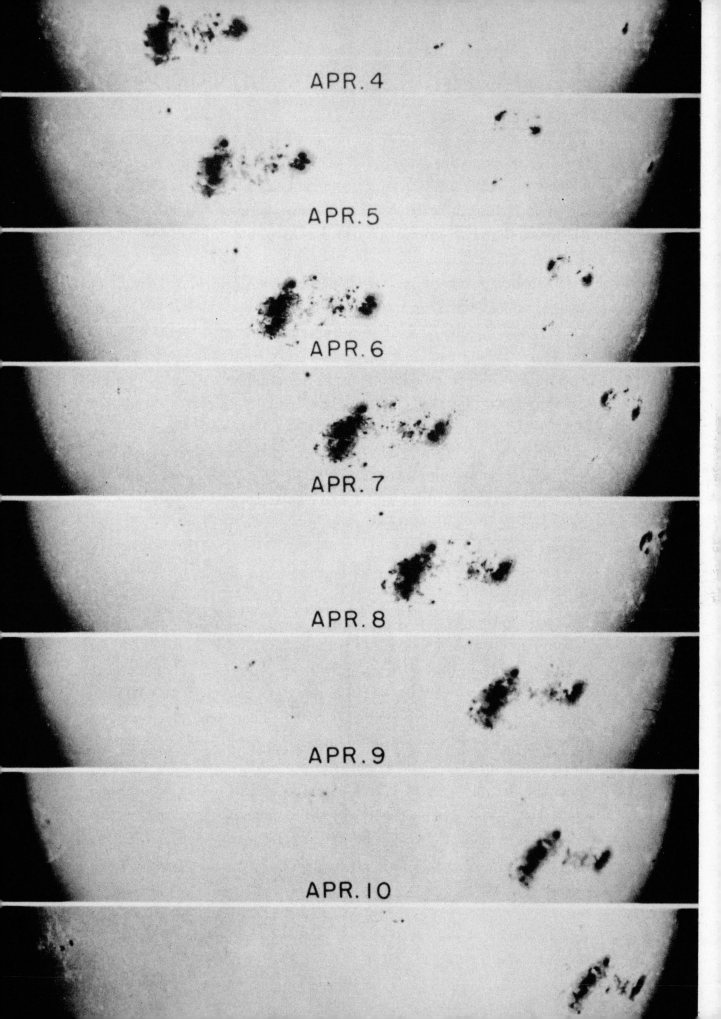

APR.4

APR.5

APR.6

APR. 7

APR.8

APR.9

APR.10

THE SUN'S STORMS—SUNSPOTS

THE PRESENCE of dark spots on the sun has been known from ancient times, even before the invention of telescopes. At times these sunspots, as we now call them, are large enough to be seen by the eye, when the sun is examined through heavily smoked or darkened glass. Sunspots might be considered the sun's "storms," though they are quite different from storms on earth.

It is believed that sunspots originate in some disturbance beneath the surface, which causes great columns of gas to rise. At the surface, the gases expand rapidly, flow outward from the center of the spot, and cause a violent, whirling motion in the surface gases around the spot. Since the gases in the sunspot are cooler than the surrounding surface, perhaps by 2,000 to 3,000° C., they appear darker. Actually sunspots are bright, but look dark by comparison to the brighter surface around them.

Strong magnetic fields develop in the area of sunspots. It is believed that the spots discharge streams or clouds of electrified gas particles into the space around the sun. Brilliant eruptions, known as flares, occur near sunspots, and huge clouds of gas can sometimes be seen drawn into sunspot regions.

The disturbances on the sun are tremendous in size, dwarfing the earth by comparison. The largest sunspots cover an area on the sun more than 30 times the surface area of the earth.

Sunspots are always found in a zone on each side of the sun's equator, extending no more than halfway to the poles of the sun. They are never seen in the vicinity of the poles. But there are certain times when few or no sunspots are seen for months at a time. Their appearance seems to follow a fairly regular cycle with an average interval of about 11 years. In this cycle, the number and extent of sunspots rise rapidly for about 4-5 years to a maximum, then decrease slowly for about 6-7 years to a minimum, after which a new cycle begins. These intervals are subject to considerable variations. New sunspot cycles began in 1944 and in 1955.

Whole solar disk and an enlargement of the great spot group of April 7, 1947
Photo: courtesy Mt. Wilson and Palomar Observatories

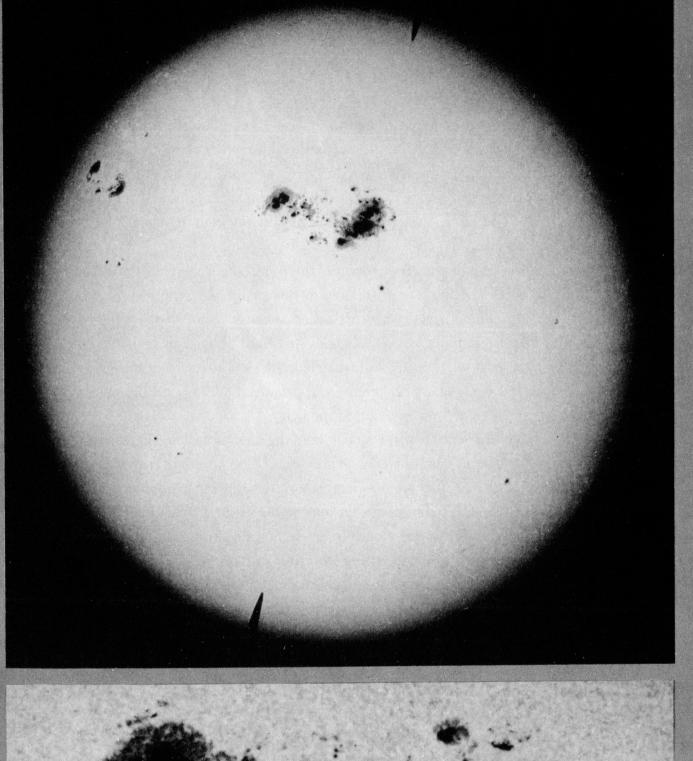
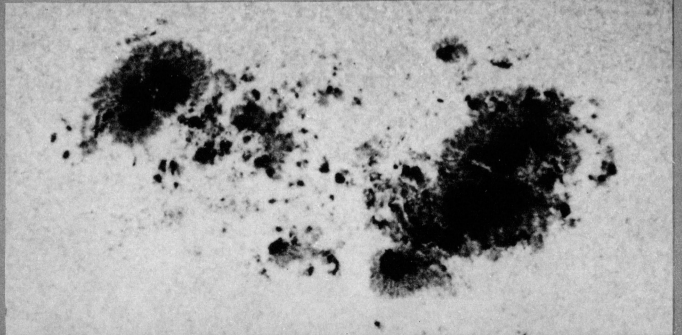

ON THE EDGE OF THE SUN

Some features of the sun stand out best when they are observed on the sun's edge. Although they are actually taking place above the surface, and could be found at nearly any position on the sun, it is when they take place along the sun's edge that they can be defined more exactly. Special equipment has been developed for blotting out the central region of the sun and allowing the edge to be studied.

Along the rim of the chromosphere, the inner atmosphere covering the sun, an ever-changing pattern of minute mountain-like eruptions of gas can·be seen. These irregularities are called *spicules*. Though they appear small, they are actually over 4,000 miles in height. They can be observed only at the edge of the sun, but occur over the entire surface. Each one seems to last up to about ten minutes, constantly building and disappearing, never the same from moment to moment.

Far more dramatic than the spicules are the enormous flame-like *prominences* that extend from the edge of the sun. These are huge eruptions or clouds of scarlet gas that seem to hang above the sun for many hours at a time, although within that time their appearance is slowly changing. They may resemble great floating clouds, huge arches, towering columns, or jet-like flames. Some seem to be rising from the surface, others appear to be fed from above and drawn into the chromosphere. They occur frequently in areas above sunspot groups. The average prominence is over 30,000 miles high, but they have been known to extend more than one million miles from the sun. When prominences occur above the surface other than at the edge, they can be detected by special means and are known as *flocculi*.

Painting: American Museum-Hayden Planetarium

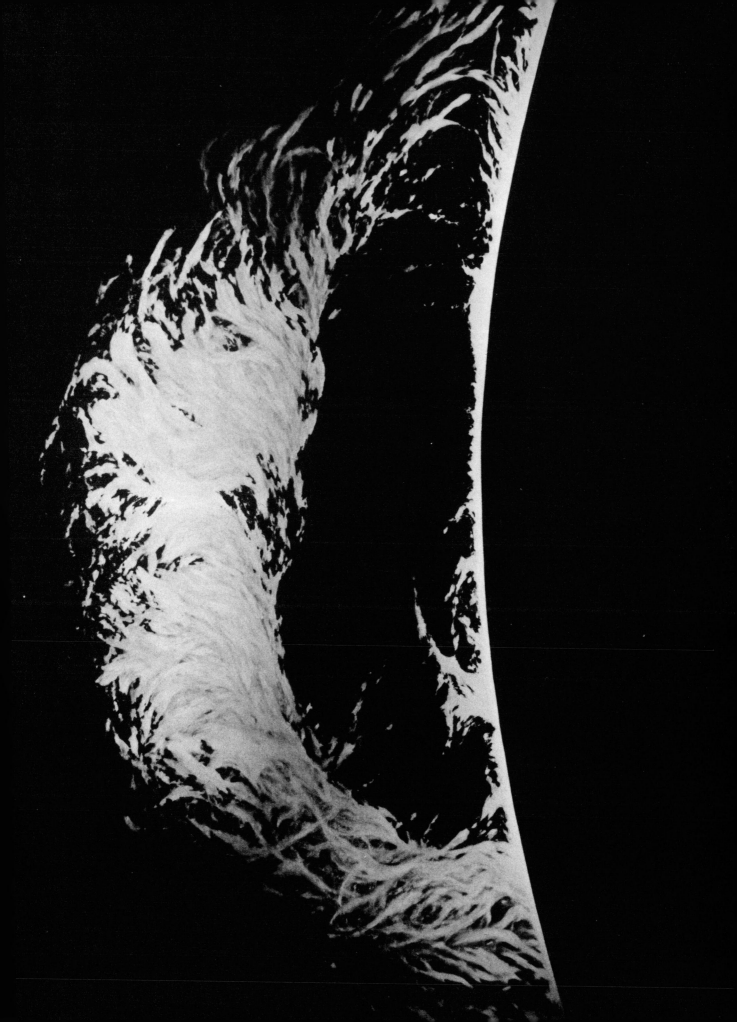

THE SUN IS AN ATOMIC MACHINE

THE SOURCE of the sun's light and heat was a mystery for many years. It is known, from evidence here on earth, that the sun has been shining for billions of years. What process and what kind of fuel could generate heat and light as intense as the sun's and continue to furnish them for that long?

Several theories have been proposed in the past: burning, contraction of the sun, or the simple cooling off of a sun that was created hot. But none of these methods could supply the sun's energy for so long. Research in radioactive processes and in the nature of the atom has led to the answer. The sun is an atomic machine, manufacturing its power by converting matter directly into energy.

One of the most fundamental laws of nature, discovered by Albert Einstein, states that matter and energy are interchangeable. A very small particle of matter potentially contains enormous quantities of energy, which can be released by the destruction of the particle. In theory, there are many ways in which this could take place, all requiring fundamental changes in the structure of atomic particles. Some of the methods have been tried on earth and have been successful.

Deep in the sun's core, atomic particles are reacting with one another, changing into atoms of a different nature, destroying some of their material in the process, and releasing the energy created by the destruction of this material.

One of the reactions which could account for the energy radiated by the sun is known as the carbon cycle. Atomic hydrogen particles, assisted by atoms of carbon, are converted into helium through a lengthy series of changes, losing some mass in the change. The lost material has been converted into energy. From the estimated amount of hydrogen in the sun and the rate of its energy production, the sun could continue to shine as it does now for 10 or 12 billion more years.

Motion of the arch prominence of June 4, 1946, one of the largest observed
Photographed in hydrogen light at the High Altitude Observatory, Climax, Colorado
Photo: Yerkes Observatory

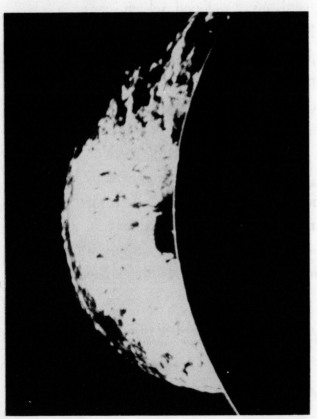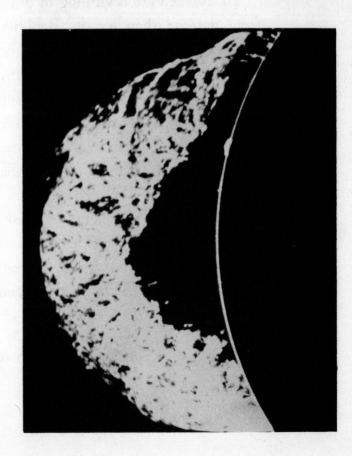

A SOLAR FURNACE

THE INFLUENCE of the sun upon the earth can be traced in many ways, some direct and others less obvious. All of the energy we use originated in the sun. Our coal and oil, and our water-powered electrical energy require the radiation of the sun for their development. The cycle of our seasons, the pattern of our weather, the rainfall upon which we depend so much, all come about through solar heating and the variations of heat during each day and year.

It is well known that changes in the sun result in changes on earth. When disturbances on the sun produce a great number of sunspots or flares, we can expect brilliant displays of northern lights, violent disturbances in the earth's magnetic field, and even complete disruption of long-range radio communications. It is suspected that periodic changes in our weather, the amount of rainfall, the growth of trees, and many other things, can be traced to slight—but not well-understood—changes in the energy the sun supplies to the earth.

Today, men are beginning to think that we can live even more directly from the sun than we do. Batteries have been developed which generate electricity when exposed to sunlight, even on cloudy days. Experiments are being conducted with many types of solar furnaces, which store up heat when they are exposed to sunlight, and release it by day or night as it is needed. Although the earth receives less than 1/2,000,000,000 of all the energy radiated by the sun, the amount it does receive is considerable. Potentially, enough energy falls on each square yard of the earth to generate about 1½ horsepower in an engine. If we consider the enormous area of the earth, the energy received from the sun could supply all of our power needs, if we could learn to use it properly. Some day there may be a solar furnace in your home, to heat it, cool it in the summer, supply it with hot water, and drive a small generator which will supply the home with all the electricity it requires.

An experimental solar furnace
Photo: courtesy High Temperature Laboratory, Fordham University, N. Y.

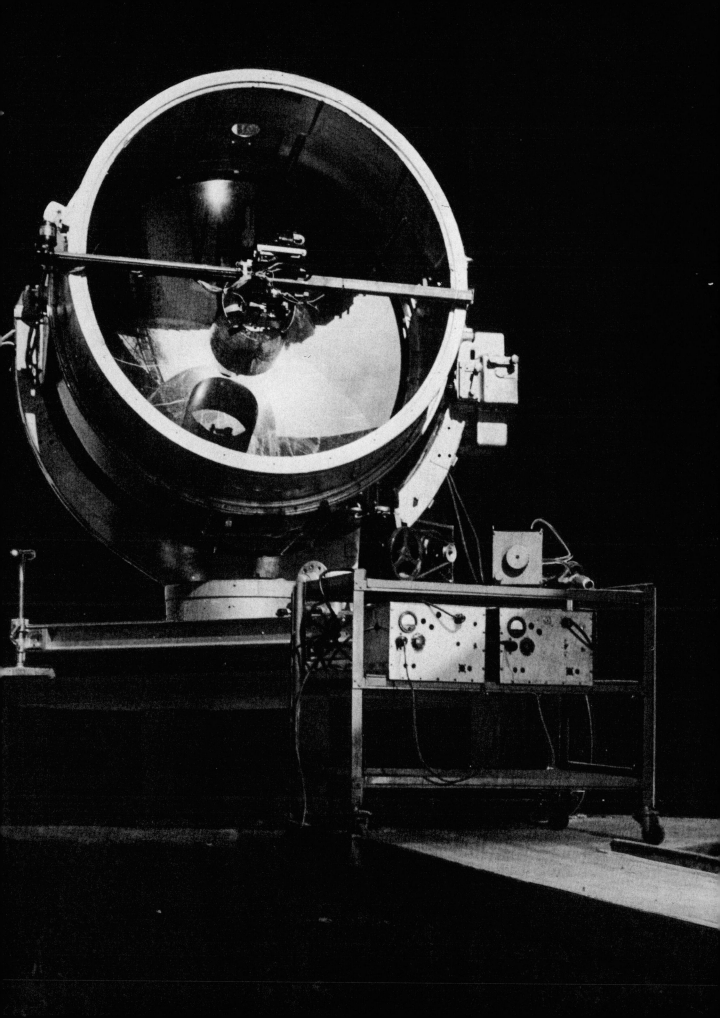

CHAPTER VI

THE MILKY WAY—OUR GALAXY

THE STARS have always fascinated and served men. Among people of ancient times, whose lives were closer to nature than ours, the stars were probably the source of both entertainment and learning in the long hours of night. Enjoyment could be found in tracing imaginary outlines of familiar figures and objects among their bright images. To those who learned to know them well, the stars served as clock, compass, and calendar, and as guides to home or to distant destinations.

Primitive seafarers, desert travelers, and wandering herdsmen saw them night after night much as we still see them now, leaving to us the inheritance of the fanciful names and figures of the constellations and names of the stars themselves.

Quite late in history, interest in the stars turned from their positions and arrangements to a concern for their nature. The story of the stars is no longer told only in legend and mythology. Today, with great telescopes and their powerful accessory tools, we learn about their distance, size, and temperature, the material of which they are made, and the physical processes that make them shine.

This chapter is the modern story of the stars of our sky, in the vast system to which they belong, the Milky Way.

WHAT IS THE MILKY WAY?

WHICHEVER WAY we look into the sky at night, there are stars. They seem to be scattered in every direction, arranged in a haphazard fashion. We could count about 3,000 of them on a clear night. With a pair of binoculars, however, the number visible would increase many times. With more powerful binoculars, or with telescopes, the number of stars we could see would continue to increase. There would be so many that it might seem there was no end, that the stars stretched out without limit.

On a very clear, dark night, a peculiar band of brightness stretches across the sky, looking like a row of faint clouds. It is like a pathway of light, circling the entire sky, but we can see only that part of it which is above the horizon. This band of light is called the Milky Way.

About 350 years ago, when Galileo looked into the sky with his first telescope, he saw that the Milky Way was made up of stars, countless millions of them. These stars are too far away to be seen as points of light, like the closer stars, except through a telescope. Yet there are so many of them that their light combines to give the appearance of hazy patches of feebly glowing brightness.

The secret of the Milky Way is the organization of the stars. Astronomers have counted the number of stars in selected parts of the Milky Way and in other parts of the sky in other directions. There are many, many more stars along the Milky Way than in any other direction in space. Locked in its mysterious glow are the clues to how many stars there are, how far out they extend, how they are arranged in space, and where the earth belongs in the universe of stars that surrounds it.

Star clouds in the Milky Way, Sagittarius region
Photographed with a Tessar lens of 10-inch focus
Photo: courtesy Mt. Wilson and Palomar Observatories

THE FORM OF OUR GALAXY

THE STARS of the Milky Way belong to a huge, wheel-shaped mass which is our galactic system, *our* Galaxy. Its shape can best be described as something like a pinwheel, with a great cloud of stars in the center and the other stars in streams that form arms spiraling around the center. From above or below, the Galaxy would look round, like a dish. Viewed on edge, it would be long and thin, like a pocket watch, but with a bulge where the large cloud of stars in the center was located.

We are living inside of this system. When we look into the Milky Way, we are looking in the direction of a great concentration of stars. Early on a summer night, there is an especially bright part of the Milky Way toward the south, in the constellation of Sagittarius, the Archer (see page 210). The center of the Galaxy, with its multitude of stars, is hidden behind vast obscuring clouds of dust and gas in that direction.

The other stars we see, those in all directions, also belong to the Galaxy. Since we are part of the Galaxy, some of its stars surround us everywhere. When we look into the sky away from the band of the Milky Way, we are looking through the thin part of the galaxy, and we can see only the stars that happen to be in the same part of the Galaxy as the sun. The Galaxy is flat and thin; there are not nearly so many stars in other directions as there are along the central plane of the Milky Way.

There are about one hundred billion stars in the Milky Way, packed densely toward the center and more thinly out toward the edge. We on earth live on a planet that circles around one of those stars, the sun. Our star is just one member of the huge family of stars that makes up this huge galactic system.

The Milky Way from Sagitta to Perseus, photographed with the Greenstein-Henyey 140° camera, 15-minute exposure
Photo: Yerkes Observatory

THE SUN IN THE MILKY WAY

IT IS IMPOSSIBLE to express distances in the Milky Way in miles. The figures would be too large to use conveniently. A different unit of measurement has been invented for this purpose. It is called a light-year. In spite of the name, a light-year measures distance, not time. It is the distance that light travels in one year, at the rate of 186,000 miles per second. Multiplying by the number of seconds in a year, one light-year is equal to about six million million miles, or about 63,000 times the distance between the earth and the sun.

Our Galaxy is about 100,000 light-years in diameter and perhaps 10,000 light-years thick. The sun is located about 30,000 light-years from the center. This would place it roughly two-thirds of the way from the center of the Galaxy towards the edge. It seems to be near the inner rim of a spiral arm, with at least one faint arm of stars further out and several others closer to the center. In terms of the thickness of the Galaxy, it is a little north of the central plane.

Like all the stars in the sky, the sun is moving. In relation to the stars nearby, it is moving about 12½ miles per second. But the whole Milky Way is rotating. The sun and the stars nearby are revolving—it appears that the sun is moving around the center of the galaxy at a speed of about 170 miles per second. In doing so, of course, it takes the earth and the whole solar system with it.

The path of the earth through space is indeed a complicated one. While we are revolving around the sun, we are also speeding on a journey around the center of the Galaxy. The Milky Way is so large, however, that even at the enormous speed of 170 miles per second the earth and the sun will take about 220 million years to complete one trip around.

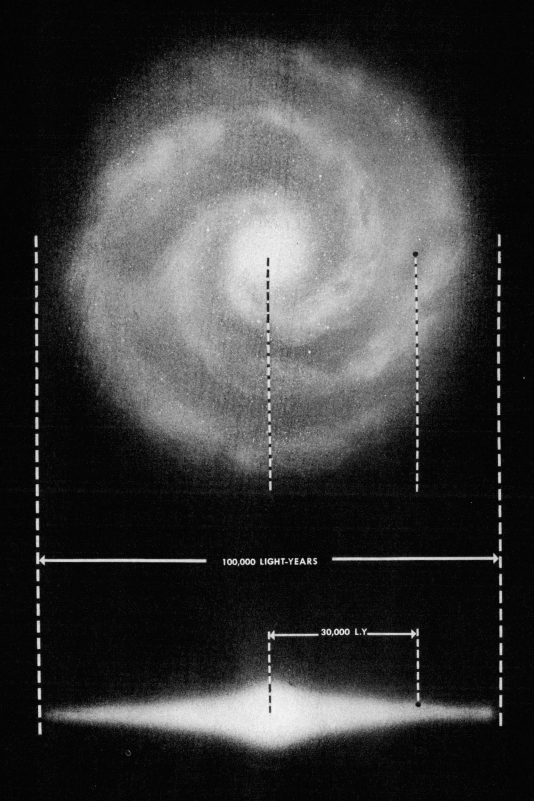

100,000 LIGHT-YEARS

30,000 L.Y.

FAMILY PORTRAIT OF THE STARS

ALL OF THE STARS in the Milky Way are like the sun in some ways, but there are many differences among them. Even with our eyes, we can see that some stars are brighter than others. In many cases this is because the bright stars are closer, but some of the brightest stars we see are not really close at all. They are just bright. There are also differences in color among the stars: red ones, yellow ones, and some that appear definitely green or blue. These are some of the ways that the stars differ from one another.

When the stars are classified by their various characteristics, such as size, temperature, amount of material in them, and brightness, many interesting relationships can be found. For one thing, the color of the stars depends on their temperature. Cooler stars are red, intermediate stars yellow, and the hottest stars are white or blue. In general, the brighter stars are also larger and hotter. The vast majority of stars can be arranged in a sequence from cool, faint stars about one-tenth as big as the sun to hot, bright stars ten times the sun's size. This group of stars is known as the "main sequence."

When main-sequence stars are classified according to color and brightness, the resulting arrangement produces a family portrait in which they can be compared. In the portrait, the small, faint stars are red and cool. As the size and brightness increase, the stars have higher temperatures, and their color is yellow, white, and blue. The sun is about in the middle of the portrait, but there are more stars below it than above. At temperatures and brightness greater than those of the sun, the number of stars decreases until we find the very few large, bright, and hot stars.

There are some stars that do not belong in this arrangement. They do not fit into the picture, and have to be classified by themselves into other groups. Some of them are called giant stars and white dwarf stars.

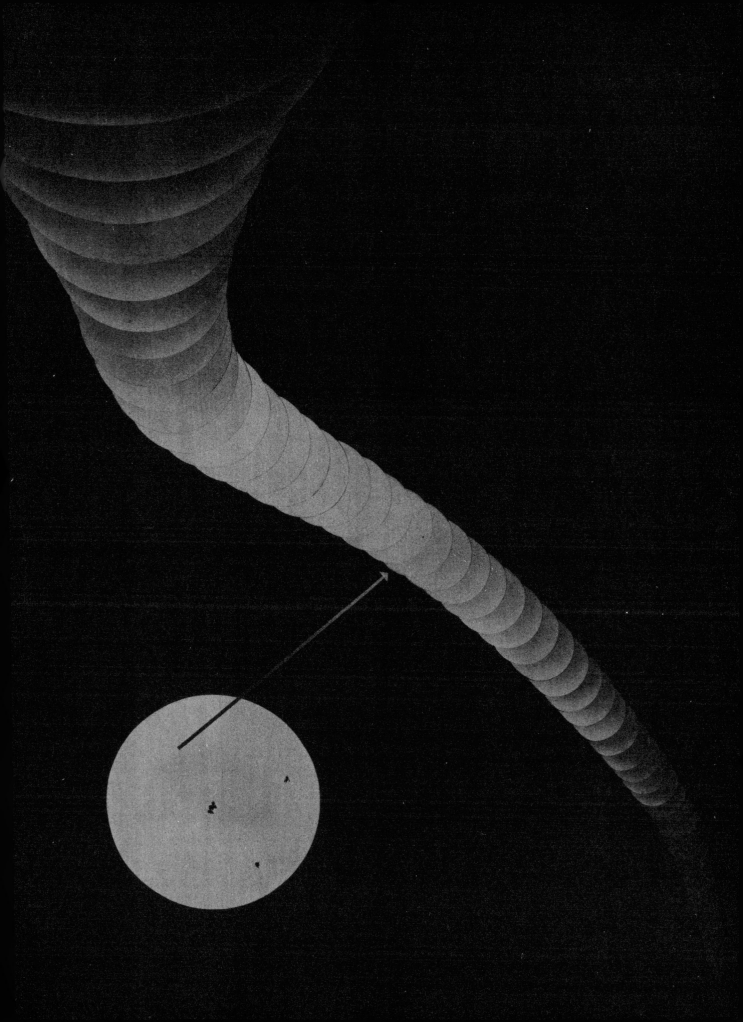

GIANT STARS

IN THE FAMILY PORTRAIT of the main-sequence stars, the large stars are bright and hot, white or blue in color. The largest would be about ten times as big as the sun and there are very few more than 100 times as bright. There is another group of stars, not so numerous as those in the main sequence, containing members much larger and brighter, but also cooler and generally yellow or red in color. These are the stars that are known as "the red giants."

A typical red giant star would be about 100 times as large as the sun, about 100-300 times as bright, and its surface would be about 1,000°-3,000° C. cooler. An example would be the star Aldebaran, the bright red star in the V-shaped group that makes up the nose of Taurus, the Bull, the constellation that is prominent during the autumn and winter (see page 214).

A very few stars are known as super-giants. Like the giants, most of them are relatively cool, but much bigger and brighter than normal stars of the same temperature. They are hundreds of times as large as the sun and thousands of times as bright. Antares, the reddish star at the heart of Scorpius, the Scorpion, easily seen toward the south on summer evenings, is a typical super-giant. Although it is nearly 3,000° C. cooler than the sun, Antares is more than 3,500 times as bright and nearly 500 times as large as the sun. If Antares could replace our sun at the center of the solar system, all of the planets out to Mars, including the earth, would revolve around beneath the surface of the star.

Although the giants and super-giants are much larger than the sun, they do not have very much more material in them. Antares has over 36 million times as much space inside of it as the sun, yet it has only about 30 times as much material as the sun does. Such a star cannot be built like the sun. It is difficult to understand how stars like that could operate as atomic machines. Perhaps they are like the sun deep inside, but are surrounded by vast envelopes of rarefied gas.

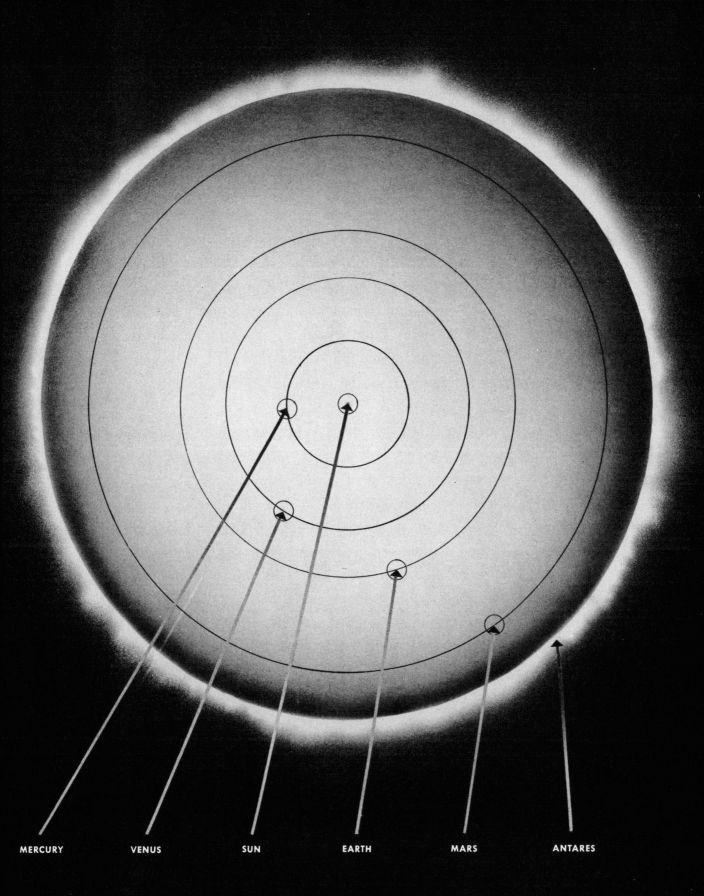

MERCURY   VENUS   SUN   EARTH   MARS   ANTARES

THE WHITE DWARF STARS

THE SMALL STARS in the family portrait are fainter than the sun and are cooler, orange or red in color. The smallest ones in the main sequence are about one-tenth as large as the sun and about one-thousandth as bright. They are known as the red dwarfs.

A number of stars have been discovered which are even smaller and do not fit into the portrait of the main sequence. Instead of being cool and red, they are hot and white, with temperatures several thousand degrees higher than the sun. These are called the white dwarfs. Very few of them are known, only about eighty, because they are difficult to recognize. Since they are so small, they are also faint, and it is impossible to see them if they are very far away. Discovery must be limited to those which are close to the earth. There are many faint stars in the sky, faint because they are far away. It is difficult to distinguish the few faint, white dwarfs which are close enough to be seen, from the many millions of other distant faint stars of the main sequence.

The smallest white dwarf discovered is known only by a catalog number. It is believed to be about half as large as the earth but it has almost three times as much material in it as the sun. For all that material to be packed into a body only about 4,000 miles in diameter, it must be incredibly dense. A portion of the star about as large as a baseball would weigh several thousand tons if placed on earth. Such a star must be constructed quite differently from the sun. One theory is that the white dwarfs may be the old stars that have become exhausted as atomic machines, and are in the process of dying out.

The picture illustrates the relative size of typical stars of the main sequence, a red giant star, and a white dwarf star. The sizes of the smaller objects are exaggerated for clarity.

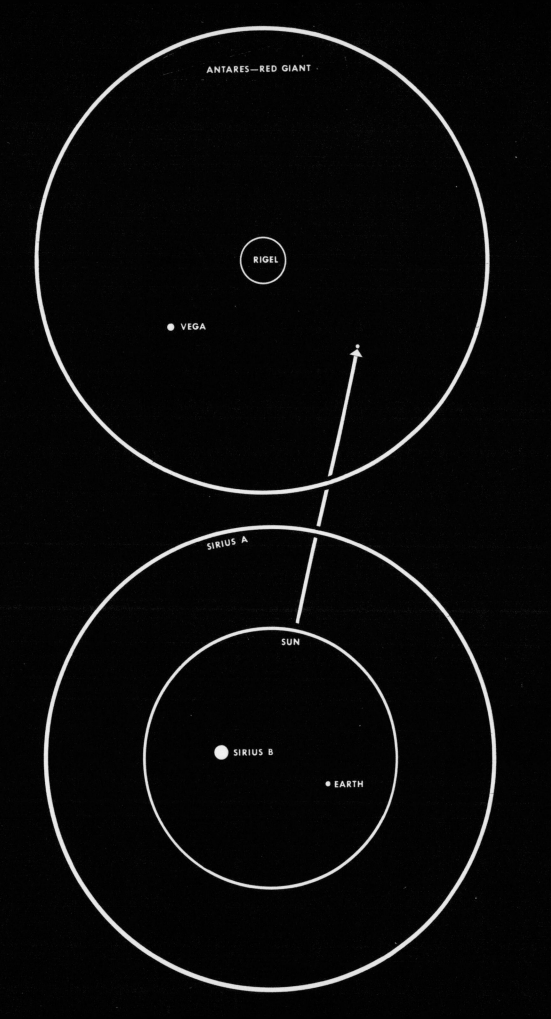

STARS THAT CHANGE
THEIR BRIGHTNESS

THE FACT that some stars change in brightness may have been suspected thousands of years ago. The first one to be recognized, however, only about 350 years ago, is a star known as Mira, which means "the marvelous." Once about every 11 months, Mira becomes as bright as the North Star, but then it fades until it cannot be seen without a telescope. Some seven thousand other stars have been discovered which behave something like Mira, having periodic changes in their brightness. These stars are called the variable stars.

The variable stars have been studied as interesting members of the star family. It has been learned that they not only change in brightness, but also in size and temperature. As they grow brighter, they seem to be expanding, and their surface grows hotter. As they grow fainter, the surface seems to recede, and they become cooler. Evidently they pulsate; some kind of mechanism is causing their envelopes to expand and contract, to grow hotter and cooler, and to grow brighter and fainter as a result.

Variable stars have been divided into several types, depending generally on the time it takes them to go through their changes. Stars like Mira are long-period variables; they have periods from 100 to 1,000 days, and many of them are somewhat irregular. Most of them are large, cool, red stars. Other stars are short-period variables; with periods from only a few hours to about fifty days. They are more regular in their changes. Still another class of variable undergoes sudden, spectacular and unpredictable changes, explosive in nature. Such a variable is called a *nova* which means a new star.

The study of variable stars is one branch of astronomy in which amateurs play an important role. Amateurs from all over the world belong to the American Association of Variable Star Observers. Their reports on the behavior of selected variable stars are sent to the headquarters at Cambridge, Massachusetts.

Photo: American Museum-Hayden Planetarium

THE CEPHEIDS

AMONG THE MOST INTERESTING of variable stars are those known as the cepheids. They are giant stars with periods of variation generally from a few days to about five weeks, with the most common period about a week. Their change in brightness is not very great, but they are quite regular and dependable in their changes. Like other variable stars, they get their name from a very bright and famous member of their type, a star of the constellation Cepheus known as Delta Cephei. Another well-known member of the cepheid family is our North Star, Polaris.

In 1912, about 100 stars of the cepheid type were discovered in the Smaller Magellanic Cloud (see page 184), the bright region in the upper portion of the photograph. Some of these stars were brighter than others, but the brightness was related to the period of the stars; the brighter the star, the longer it took from one maximum brightness to the next. Since the stars were all about the same distance away, the differences in brightness were not caused by distance; they must have been related to the nature of the stars themselves.

How bright these stars really were, of course, was not known, because no one knew how far away they were. Astronomers have since succeeded in estimating the distance to some other cepheid variables, so that their true brightness, and its relation to their period, is now known.

Thus the period-brightness relation of the cepheid variable star has become a most valuable device for measuring extremely great distances in the universe. The distance scale determined by the period-luminosity relationship among cepheid variables depends on estimates of the luminosity, the intrinsic brightness, of the cepheid stars. Several revisions of the scale have been necessary since earlier values, as new data concerning luminosity became available. These revisions have resulted in new estimates of distances and populations in the areas of space reached by great telescopes.

Photographed at Harvard's Boyden Station, South Africa
Photo: Yerkes Observatory

THE REMAINS OF A SUPERNOVA

About 100 novae have been detected among the stars in our Milky Way. There may have been others too faint to be recognized, but they are still a rather small percentage of the hundred billion stars in the system. A nova is a relatively rare thing.

An ordinary nova loses very little material in its explosion, probably less than a tenth of one percent. When it dies down, it returns to its former brightness and condition, practically unchanged. But a *supernova* undergoes a great change. The amount of energy it releases is more than the energy in the average star. There is evidence that a supernova may be a giant star that suddenly becomes transformed into a white dwarf star, losing most of its material in the outburst.

No other object in the sky looks quite like the Crab Nebula, the picture on the opposite page. It is a shell of gases, with a very complicated structure, about 4,000 light-years away. There is a faint blue star near its center. The gases seem to be expanding outward from that star at a speed of about 800 miles per second. Tracing backwards, it would seem that the Crab Nebula must have originated from an explosion in that star about 900 years ago.

Ancient Chinese and Japanese records show that a "guest" star, or nova, appeared on July 4, 1054 in a location that corresponds to the position of the Crab Nebula. The records reported that the star became as bright as the planet Venus, the brightest thing we ever see at night, except the moon. If that nova was the faint blue star in the center of the Crab Nebula, then it must have exploded so violently that it became 300 million times as bright as the sun. Such an object is known as a supernova. The Crab Nebula is the remains of the supernova of 1054.

Only three such stars brilliant enough to be classed as supernovae have been known to occur in the Milky Way. That of 1054 was the first. In 1572, Tycho Brahe reported another that became bright enough to be seen in the daytime. A third was reported by another astronomer, Kepler, in the year 1604; it became the brightest star in the sky. Each of these increased its usual brightness by millions of times.

Photo: courtesy Mt. Wilson and Palomar Observatories; 200-inch photograph

DOUBLE STARS

STARS ARE FOUND arranged in groups more often than they are found to be alone. It is very common to find stars in pairs; sometimes a third or fourth star will make them multiple; and in some places in the sky hundreds of stars are organized into clusters. All the stars in our sky, of course, belong to the Milky Way. These groupings are not just accidental locations of stars in the same direction; they are formed of stars which remain together in a permanent bond.

Pairs of stars are known as double stars. Some appear double because they look close in the sky, but they need not be. If you can find the Big Dipper, look at the middle star in the handle, Mizar. You may see a faint star very close to it, called Alcor. These two look close but they are not companions. They just happen to be in the same direction as seen from the earth, but Alcor is actually far away from Mizar.

Mizar is a double star, but its companion is not Alcor. Mizar is really two stars so close that they look like one, but they can be seen separately in a telescope. The two stars are moving around each other, and they are permanently held together by their mutual gravitational attraction. Many other bright stars are like that, such as Polaris, Albireo, Castor, and even the brightest star, Sirius. A great percentage of the stars, perhaps even the majority, are really double stars. Some examples are shown in the picture.

Sometimes a star is known to be double because it changes its brightness in a strange way. It might be called a variable star also, but it is not really variable in itself. The change in brightness comes about when one of the companions passes in front of the other, cutting off its light. Such a star is known as an Algol-type variable, from a bright, well-known star of that kind called Algol. An Algol variable might look like one star even in the largest of telescopes, but it can be recognized as double because of the way it seems to change its brightness.

Photo: Yerkes Observatory

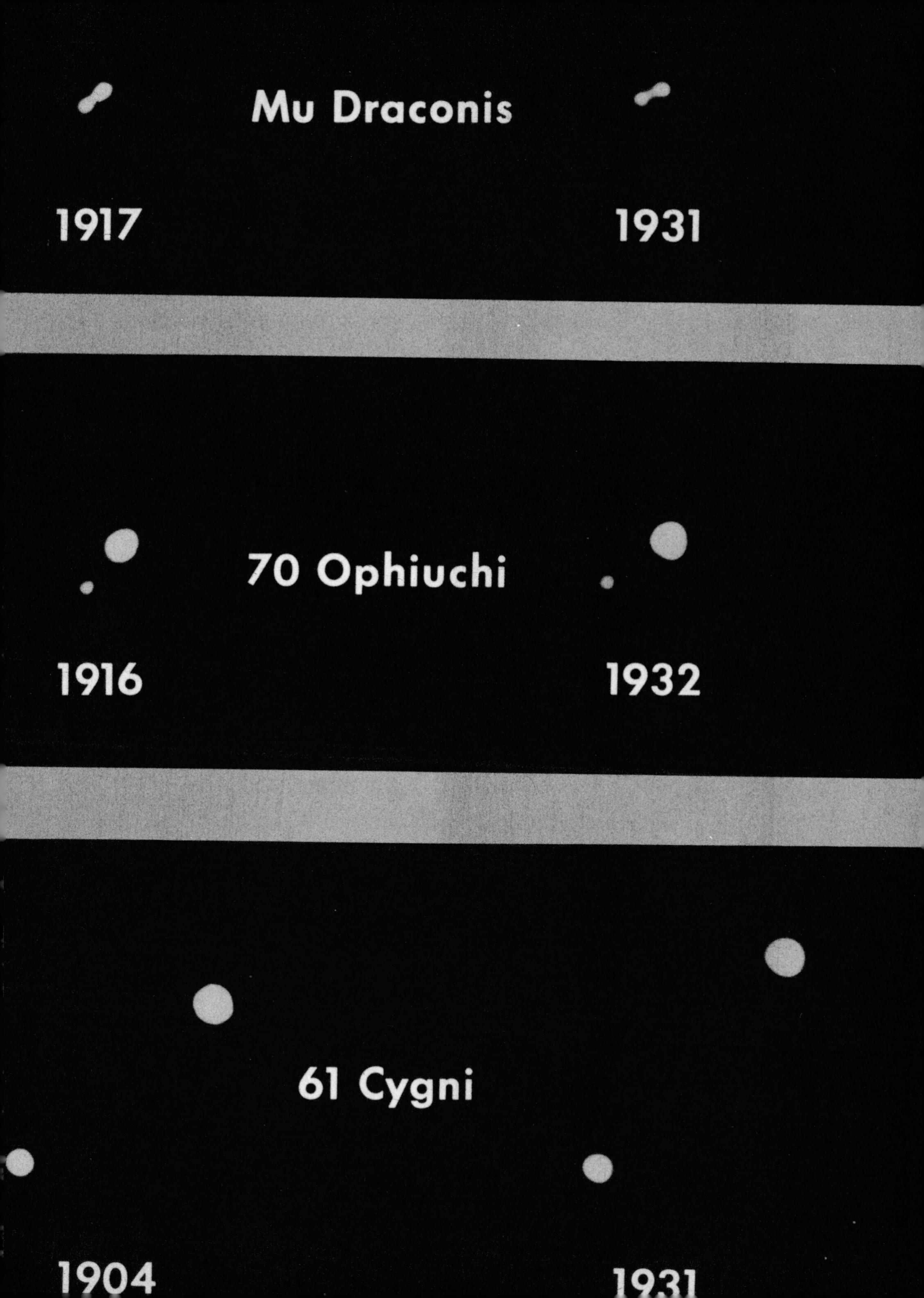

Mu Draconis

1917

1931

70 Ophiuchi

1916

1932

61 Cygni

1904

1931

SIRIUS AND ITS COMPANION

ALTHOUGH stars are moving hundreds of miles per second, we cannot see that motion because they are so far away. Astronomers have learned to detect it, however, at least for the closer stars. Normally they move in a regular manner, but if a star is found that seems to be moving in a wavy line, it is suspected of being a double star. The gravitational attraction of an unseen companion could account for the irregular motion of the star.

That is how Sirius, the brightest star we see, was found to be double. Its peculiar motion was observed before 1850, and a companion moving around it in a period of 50 years was predicted. The very faint companion was found in 1862. Since Sirius is called the "Dog Star," its companion was nicknamed the "Pup." Sirius is brighter and hotter than the sun and about twice as large, a member of the main sequence. Its companion, however, is a very dense, small, white dwarf.

The companion follows a wavy line just like Sirius, but even more pronounced. By watching the movements of the stars in the sky, astronomers have been able to picture the way they move around each other. Actually, both of the stars are moving around a third point, where the center of gravity of the two is located. They move in balance; when Sirius is on one side of the center of gravity, the companion is about twice as far away on the other side, since its mass is less than half that of Sirius.

In the illustration, adapted from a drawing by Van Biesbroeck, the path of the white dwarf companion is referred to the position of Sirius, based on observations of the companion's positions from 1862 to 1913. The mean orbit shown is derived from the plotted positions. True space motion of both stars is more complex.

Photo: Adapted from Yerkes Observatory photograph

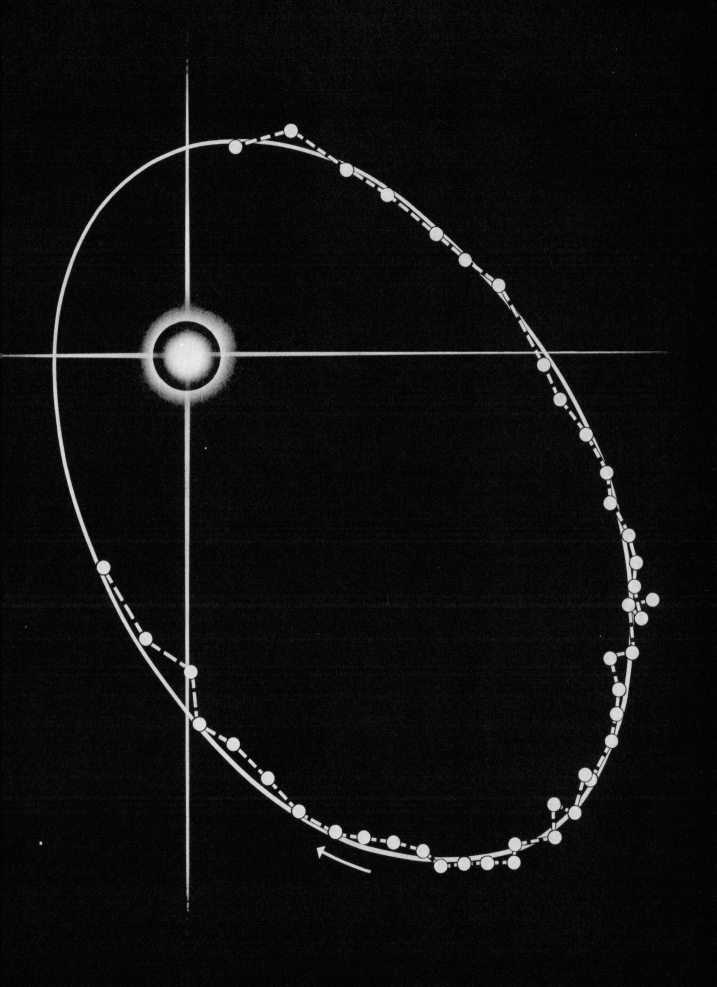

MULTIPLE STARS

Sometimes the companions of a double star are found to be double in themselves. The star then becomes known as multiple—made up of several stars quite close together, all moving around the mutual center of gravity of the system. Such well-known stars as Mizar, Castor, Alpha Centauri, and even the North Star, Polaris, are known to be multiple stars.

Castor is a very bright, white star in the winter sky, one of the two stars known as the Twins, Castor and Pollux. The two stars are not gravitationally or physically related to each other. Castor itself has been known as a double star for many years. Even a small telescope shows the two stars of the system, both hot, white stars. They are going around each other in a period of about 380 years.

However, each one of these companions is really two stars quite close together and also moving around one another, one pair in about nine days and the other in about three days.

This is already a rather complicated system, but there are even more members. Not far from Castor, the telescope shows a faint red star which also appears to belong to the system. It is so far away from Castor, however, that it must take about 10,000 years to complete a revolution. This star is also a double star. It consists of two stars going around each other in less than a day. They are very close together, perhaps almost touching, and they must be pulled out of shape by the gravitational force between the two.

That makes six stars in the Castor system, three pairs of stars moving around the mutual center of gravity of the group. Many more stars are known to be multiple, and there are even more complex systems than the Castor group.

Not all double stars can be resolved visually into their components, especially if the two stars are quite close. Some of them can be detected by unusual features of their spectra. They are then called spectroscopic doubles. This is often the case in discovering the multiple nature of a visual double, such as Castor.

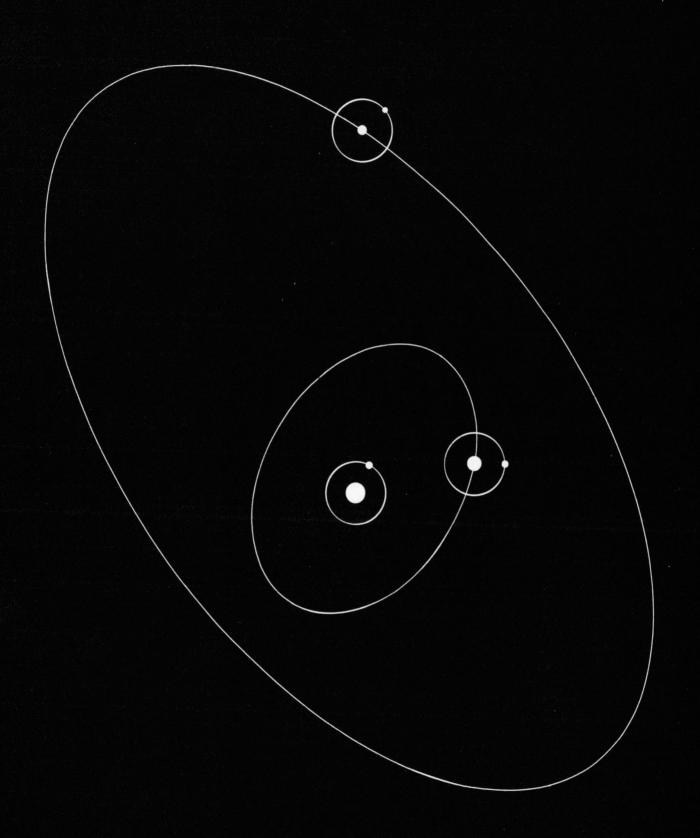

CLUSTERS OF STARS

Most of us know the little group of close stars that are known as "The Seven Sisters." The stars are bright and easily seen, but only six of them can be counted readily, the six brightest in the photograph. It seems obvious that they belong to some kind of group. Astronomers have confirmed this by carefully measuring their motions. The stars we call the Seven Sisters, and many other stars nearby but fainter, are all moving through space in the same direction and at about the same speed.

A group of stars like that is known as a cluster of stars. The cluster that contains the Seven Sisters is called the Pleiades. There are over 250 stars in the cluster, located about 500 light-years away. Another star cluster that can be seen easily is known as the Hyades, the V-shaped group of stars near the Pleiades. The bright red star Aldebaran looks like one of the group but actually it is not, it just happens to be located in the same direction.

Over 400 clusters of stars like the Pleiades are known in our star system. Most of them have over 100 star members, loosely organized in what we might think of as a "flock" of stars. They are often called open clusters. All of them are located generally in the direction of the Milky Way, and they are also known as Galactic Clusters. The stars in the cluster are actually quite far apart, and it is entirely possible that other stars might pass through it for a time, without disturbing the progress of the cluster.

Five of the stars in the Big Dipper, some about 80 light-years away, and a great many other nearby stars, belong to the Ursa Major cluster. But the brightest star Sirius, about 8½ light-years away in the southern sky, shares the same motion. It is evidently another member of the Ursa Major cluster, though it hardly appears like it from its location in our sky. Some astronomers believe that the sun is also a member of this same cluster.

Photo: courtesy Mt. Wilson and Palomar Observatories; 18-inch Schmidt photograph

THE GLOBULAR CLUSTERS

ABOUT 150 years ago, the great astronomer Sir William Herschel was "sweeping" the heavens, observing and recording anything unusual or of special interest he could find in the sky. While doing so he came across several strikingly beautiful objects that looked like huge balls of stars. The stars were so numerous that the center of each ball resembled a brilliant mass of light. Countless other stars shone round the center like a halo. These groups of stars became known as the globular clusters. The photograph shows the globular cluster Messier 13, in the constellation of Hercules.

At the present time, about 100 globular clusters have been discovered. They are quite unlike the open-type clusters, such as the Pleiades and the Hyades. Instead of hundreds of stars, the globular clusters contain thousands or hundreds of thousands. All of them have the same shape, like balls or slightly flattened spheres, with the greatest concentration of stars toward the center. The globular clusters are much further away than the open-type clusters that we know. The nearest is about 20,000 light-years from us and the most distant discovered is over 100,000 light-years. In spite of their great distance, however, they are so brilliant that some of them can be seen without a telescope.

The most unusual feature about the globular clusters is that they all seem to be located in one direction in our sky, toward the southern stars of the summer, where the center of the Milky Way is located. Since we are located on the side of the Milky Way, far from the center, we can expect that these objects are concentrated near the center. But the globular clusters are found some distance above or below the Milky Way, and they do not seem to share the motion of the spiral arms about the center. They are thought to be part of a kind of framework around the Milky Way, with a motion and an organization quite different from the stars and clusters of stars that make up the spiral arms.

Photo: Mt. Wilson and Palomar Observatories; 200-inch photograph

STAR POPULATIONS

When astronomers prepare the family portrait of stars near the sun, they obtain a picture like the one on page 153. The stars in open clusters, such as the Pleiades, also display the same type of portrait. They are the stars that form the spiral arms of the Milky Way.

The globular clusters, from their location, do not belong to the system of spiral arms. Many other stars, typical of those in the globular clusters, are concentrated toward the center of the Milky Way, but above or below the plane of the spiral arms. These stars, and the globular clusters seem to be moving in a different way from the stars in the spiral arms. They do not share the rotation of the arms about the center of the galaxy. It seems that they form a kind of halo about the center, almost spherical in shape.

If the size, brightness, color, and temperature of these stars are arranged in a family portrait, the picture becomes entirely different from the ones we have discussed. Among these stars that seem to be outside of the spiral arms, the larger and brighter stars are cooler and redder, and most of the stars are brighter and larger than the sun.

Astronomers now think of two different populations of stars, perhaps with different origins or with different life histories. The stars of the spiral arms, that rotate about the center of the Milky Way in the arms, and which display the familiar family portrait, are known as Population I. These seem to be newer stars, still in the process of development, and perhaps still forming. The stars of the globular clusters, and those concentrated in an aura about the center of the galaxy, which do not share the motion of the spiral arms, and which have an entirely different set of characteristics, belong to Population II. These stars seem to be older. They may have been the early stars formed in the Milky Way, and are now in a far more advanced stage of evolution than the stars of Population I.

CLOUDS OF BRIGHT GAS

THE MILKY WAY contains a great many stars, and the stars contain enormous quantities of material in them. But stars do not comprise the entire mass of the system. Additional material is scattered in the space between them as very rarefied gas, minute solid particles, and dust. Clouds of this nebulous material (so-called because it is so thinly scattered) dim the stars at great distances, hide many parts of the Milky Way, and prevent us entirely from seeing the brilliant center of the galaxy and the region beyond the center.

The presence of this gaseous material in space was discovered soon after the invention of the telescope, although its nature was not known immediately. Hazy, bright, extended objects, as far away as the stars, were observed and given the name *nebulae* to distinguish them from stars.

Subsequently, some of these nebulae were found to be clouds of stars at great distances, such as the globular clusters described on page 172, and the exterior galaxies treated in Chapter VII. But, in 1864, William Huggins, a pioneer in the use of the spectroscope in astronomy, showed that at least some of the nebulae were clouds of glowing gases. The spectrum of a star or a star cloud exhibits a continuous bright background interrupted by dark lines, but the gaseous nebulae show a series of bright lines, without the continuous background.

The most conspicuous of the gaseous nebulae is the Great Nebula in Orion, shown here. It appears to the eye as the middle star in the Sword of Orion, somewhat fuzzy compared to the other stars. But in a telescope it becomes an extended region of brightly glowing gases, slightly green in color.

Photo: courtesy Mt. Wilson and Palomar Observatories; 100-inch photograph

THE NORTH AMERICA NEBULA

THE GREAT NEBULA in Orion is bright enough to be seen without a telescope, but most of the gaseous nebulae are much fainter. Many of them are revealed only on photographic plates after long exposure at the focus of a telescope. In recent years, a great many bright nebulae have been found in this manner.

Some of the nebulae are named for the constellation in which they are found. Others are known only by the numbers assigned to them in the catalogs of such objects. Still others are given special names because of their resemblance to familiar shapes and patterns. The bright region shown here, found in the constellation Cygnus, not far from the bright star Deneb, is often called the North America Nebula, because the outline of the North American continent can be traced in its regions of brightness. It is also referred to by catalog as N.G.C. 7,000 (nebula number 7,000 in the New General Catalog). The brightness of the nebulae has been explained in several ways. Clouds of gas, like the Great Nebula in Orion, are probably excited by the energy of stars within or near the cloud. The gaseous material absorbs stellar energy and re-emits the energy as light. If solid particles or dust are also present with the gas, some of the starlight may be scattered and reflected by the solid material to contribute to the brightness of the nebula.

In very extended, glowing regions like the North America Nebula, another process contributes to the illumination. It is believed that some of the light-producing energy comes from the collision of particles in motion within the clouds. The brightness in some nebulae is produced solely by this process.

Photo: National Geographic Society-Palomar Observatory Sky Survey;
48-inch Schmidt photograph

DARK CLOUDS

WHERE DUST and minute solid particles are scattered through the gas in space, the clouds of material may completely hide everything that lies behind them. Whole regions of the sky appear to be almost completely devoid of stars. At one time, it was thought that these dark regions might be holes or tunnels through the stars, but it is now known that the apparent holes are caused by dark, obscuring clouds of material lying between us and more distant stars.

Most of the constellation Orion, which contains the most familiar group of bright stars in the winter sky, seems to be imbedded in thinly scattered gas and dust clouds, at a distance of about 1,500 light-years. In several parts of the sky within the boundaries of Orion, dark patches appear with very few stars, adjacent to other bright areas and areas which appear to have many more stars.

The region shown in this photograph includes the Horsehead Nebula, in Orion. The name is given because of the shape in the prominent dark cloud at the center of the picture. When the picture is held sideways, the appearance of the horse's head becomes more apparent.

The dark material in the left half of the region hides all but the nearest stars. On the right, however, many faint stars, far and near, can be observed. The Horsehead extends like a great dark bay into the brightness. The line of glowing material extending down through the center of the area appears to be the junction of the two clouds, and may be glowing because of the energy of collision among the particles.

This region is not conspicuous, even in a telescope. It requires long exposure on a photographic plate to record what you see here.

Photo: courtesy Mt. Wilson and Palomar Observatories; 200-inch photograph

CHAPTER VII

OTHER GALAXIES

No ONE KNOWS where man's quest for knowledge will eventually take him, or what kind of a universe it may ultimately reveal. It has already led him downward in size to the basic structure of all matter, the atom and its sub-particles. It has also led up the scale of size to the discovery of the vast systems of stars known as galaxies.

Whatever the picture of the universe science may finally yield, the organization of matter into galaxies dominates the scene today. These enormous star systems seem to be building-blocks in the architecture of space.

The description of the galactic universe on the following pages reaches toward the frontier of modern astronomy.

HOW MANY GALAXIES?

No ONE WOULD DARE to answer this question! Our knowledge of the universe, the depth to which it is probed by modern instruments, and the interpretation of what the telescope reveals—all these factors are changing so rapidly that any statement made here might well be out of date in a few years, even in a few months.

Only three galaxies beyond our own can be seen without telescopic assistance. Two appear as vast stellar clouds over the Southern Hemisphere, and were named for the explorer Magellan. The larger Magellanic Cloud, appearing to be about 7° in diameter (14 times the apparent diameter of the sun) is estimated to have an actual diameter of 30,000 light-years, and to lie outside the fringes of the southern Milky Way at a distance of nearly 150,000 light-years. The smaller cloud appears a little more than half as large, and is slightly more distant. Both have been incorrectly considered as part of our Milky Way.

A few degrees northeast of the star Alpheratz, one can spot a hazy blur of light in the summer sky. On a clear night, away from city lights, it can be seen distinctly. It is the Andromeda galaxy. With the exception of these three objects (the two Magellanic Clouds and the Andromeda galaxy), everything we see with our unaided eyes is part of the Milky Way system.

In our own vicinity, there are seventeen galaxies located within a region 2,000,000 light-years in diameter, including the three mentioned above and the Milky Way. This is referred to as our "local group." It may be a cluster of galaxies, and the population may not be representative of the density of galaxies in other parts of space. Several thousand more "cities of stars" are near enough for their structure to be studied with our present telescopes. Within a distance of 250,000,000 light-years, it is estimated that there are about *two billion galaxies,* and that is not the end of the presently visible universe.

Four galaxies in the constellation of Leo; 200-inch photograph
Photo: courtesy Mt. Wilson and Palomar Observatories

DISTANCES BETWEEN GALAXIES

THE GALAXIES are all so far from us that we cannot possibly determine the distances between them by using a base-line from trigonometry. The trigonometric methods of distance determination fail even within the Milky Way, except for the nearest stars. About 40 years ago, some Harvard astronomers found a relationship between the distance and the changes in brightness of the cepheid variables (see page 160), and thus were able to estimate the distance to any galaxy where this kind of star could be identified. Fortunately, the cepheid appears commonly. A distance scale for the universe was devised in which the Andromeda galaxy, for example, was found to be 700,000 light-years from the Milky Way.

In 1952, Walter Baade of Mount Wilson and Palomar Observatories, found that the cepheid distance scale was in error, that earlier values had to be increased by a factor of at least two, perhaps more. The distance between our Milky Way and the Andromeda galaxy, or between any two galaxies must be revised upward. Based on present knowledge, a distance of a little more than two million light-years to the Andromeda galaxy is a good estimate.

Another result of the change in scale is that our estimates of the size and brightness of the galaxies must be increased in proportion. To provide the amount of light that we can see, at *twice* the distance, the object itself must be four times as bright, and to appear as it does, it must be larger than formerly believed. An estimate of distances and relative dimensions of some nearer galaxies is shown in the artist's diagram here.

But, most important, the dimensions of the known universe itself must be increased. The 200-inch telescope can gather light not from a distance of one billion light-years as was earlier thought, but *two*. The diameter of our observable sphere has reached the huge figure of four billion light-years.

Photo: American Museum-Hayden Planetarium

OUR GALAXY

MAGELLANIC
CLOUDS

147
185

SCULPTOR

ANDROMEDA
GALAXY AND
COMPANIONS

M 33

FORNAX

5822

IC 1613

THE ANDROMEDA GALAXY— MESSIER 31

AMONG THE NEARBY galaxies in the local group described on page 184, the Andromeda galaxy—Messier 31—is the most dominant. It can be seen through the stars of Andromeda on a clear summer evening, and it was long known as a nebula, for it does look like a cloud of interstellar gas. It is now properly known as a galaxy—an aggregation of billions of stars related to one another by mutual gravitation.

The Andromeda galaxy has often been thought of as a mirror image of our own Milky Way. Without doubt there are similarities: both appear to belong to the same celestial family tree. Each has a concentration of stars in the central portions, and the spiral arms wound loosely around this nucleus. There are stars of many spectral types, globular clusters, novae, bright glowing gases, dust, and cepheids. Population I stars and interstellar gas are found in the spiral arms, and Population II stars near the center. Messier 31 is like the Milky Way in another respect. It has two small galaxies near its edges that remind us of the Magellanic Clouds. They are Messier 32 and NGC 205 (neither has a popular name, only catalog numbers).

The Andromeda galaxy is also similar to the Milky Way in size. Its diameter is about 2° of arc, and at the distance now recorded, the system must be just a little larger than ours.

The plane of this galaxy is tilted about 15° to a line of sight from the earth. We can, therefore, see the entire configuration reasonably well, and can easily identify the concentrations of stars in the spiral arms. The average individual stars cannot be identified, however. At this great distance, stars that are some 1,500 times brighter than our sun cannot be distinguished clearly even with the 200-inch telescope.

Photo: courtesy Mt. Wilson and Palomar Observatories; 48-inch Schmidt photograph

OTHER SPIRAL GALAXIES

A GREAT MAJORITY of the distant galaxies are spirals. They possess a disk-like shape that can be likened to a wheel with a large hub at the center. Both the Milky Way and the Andromeda galaxy are typical examples of the spiral systems. However, we cannot examine the Milky Way well because we are in it, and much of its structure is obscured by intervening gases and stars. The Andromeda spiral is inclined to our line of sight, as can be noted on the previous page, and is also difficult to study in some respects.

The beautiful "whirlpool" galaxy in Canes Venatici, shown on the opposite page, is oriented in space so that we look down on it directly. We can see the nearly symmetrical arrangement of the spiral arms—the manner in which they encircle the nucleus for more than 360°. Clouds of dark, gaseous material can be seen between the arms, and bright nebulae are obvious in the arms.

Some spiral galaxies are viewed edge-on. Where this is true, the brilliant elliptical concentration of stars in the central portions can be seen extending above and below the plane defined by the spiral arms. The nucleus is the thickest part, the hub of the wheel.

About one spiral galaxy in three has a "bar" extending outward from the nucleus (see photograph on page 201). The spiral arms originate at the end of the bars, and then form the same pattern as in the normal spirals. Some of the spirals are loosely wound, others are tight and compact. In some the nucleus stands out brilliantly, as in the galaxy in Canes Venatici; in others, light is quite evenly distributed across the entire galaxy. Each of the thousands photographed to date has its own individual characteristics. No two are alike.

Photo: courtesy Mt. Wilson and Palomar Observatories; 200-inch photograph

ELLIPTICAL GALAXIES

NOT ALL GALAXIES have the familiar spiral structure. A significant number, in fact, are so greatly different from the spirals that they have to be treated separately. Usually they are referred to as elliptical galaxies, a phrase that describes them rather well. The stars of which they consist are concentrated in great homogeneous masses that are ellipsoidal, or nearly spheroid in form. In recent years some of them have been photographed so skillfully that individual stars have been identified in the outermost fringes. Near the center there are so many stars that it is impossible to separate them photographically.

The elliptical galaxies seem to contain only Population II-type stars, and are therefore similar to the nuclei of the normal spirals. There is little interstellar gas such as that which abounds in the Milky Way and elsewhere. Because of the absence of this obscuring gas, it is even possible to see through some of the smaller ones.

One of these elliptical systems, in the constellation of Sculptor, is nearer to us than any exterior star systems except the Magellanic Clouds. It is only a few thousand light-years in diameter. Yet some of the elliptical galaxies rival the great spirals in dimensions. An example is Messier 87 (the 87th celestial object listed in Charles Messier's catalog of 1784) in the constellation of Virgo, shown on the opposite page. Surrounding it are a number of bright objects that seem to be similar to the globular clusters scattered about the center of the Milky Way. Smaller elliptical galaxies are more numerous than the massive type like M87.

During the past few years, it has been determined that M87 is a source of radio energy, a distinction shared with very few galaxies investigated to date.

Photo: courtesy Mt. Wilson and Palomar Observatories; 200-inch photograph

DIMENSIONS OF GALAXIES

WHEN THE DISTANCE to an object is known, and the dimensions as they appear to the eye or through a telescope have been determined, then the actual dimensions of that object can be calculated. For example, a large cloud at a great distance may seem small and unimportant, but it may cover the entire sky of those people beneath it. Knowledge of the distances between galaxies is essential if we are to know their true dimensions. By using Baade's distance scale, we can make some good estimates about the size characteristics of some of these distant star groups.

Like the Milky Way, all of the other galaxies are fantastically large. Light energy, traveling 186,000 miles each second, commonly requires 100,000 years to pass from one side of a galactic system to the other. The least dimension is usually of the order of several thousand light-years. There are, of course, great differences; some smaller galaxies may be only 4,000 to 8,000 light-years in diameter, while the larger ones may have a diameter of 200,000 light-years.

There are differences in size among the different types of systems. The spiral galaxies, on the average, are larger than the irregular or elliptical ones. An interesting comparison of galactic dimensions involves the Andromeda galaxy and the smaller of the two elliptical galaxies that appear to be associated with it. The greatest diameter of the Andromeda system is about 130,000 light-years, while that of the "satellite" group NCG 205 is only about 5,000 light-years.

These values all depend on the accuracy of distance measurements. If our scale based on the cepheids were to be changed again, as it was in 1952, all dimensions would have to be re-calculated.

Spiral galaxy in Coma Berenices, seen edge on
Photo: courtesy Mt. Wilson and Palomar Observatories; 200-inch photograph

LIFE HISTORY OF GALAXIES

WHEN WE LOOK AROUND in our visible universe and find the several different kinds of galaxies—the spirals and the barred spirals, the large and small elliptical types, and the irregular Magellanic-type—we can't help but wonder if there is a life sequence among them. Is it not likely that one of the types is old, and another new? Might we be looking at some star systems that are about to expire, and others that are just beginning an active life?

Any answer to such questions must be highly speculative, for we have been studying these distant star groups in detail for only a little more than half a century, a fleeting instant in the billions of years of existence which they represent. Yet there are a few clues which permit us to guess about the beginnings and endings of stars and their "cities."

We might start with the assumption that the universe as we know it began with a great explosion. There are many who question this assumption; some believe that matter is being created continuously. If the galaxies all did form as the result of the great explosion, then there are no older or younger ones as judged by years only. Some may be more advanced than others, however, and it is believed by some theorists that the irregular galaxies are least advanced.

The elliptical galaxies may be most mature and contain Population II stars that were formed very early. In the spiral systems in rapid rotation, only part of the gas and dust from the explosion became stars immediately; much of the gas and dust still remains. This material now exists chiefly in the spiral arms and it is even today being used up in the formation of newer Population I stars. We might think of the stars in the spiral arms of the Milky Way as being among the "younger" objects in the universe.

Types of galaxies, normal and barred spirals
Photo: courtesy Mt. Wilson and Palomar Observatories; 60-inch photograph

Sa NGC 4594

SBa NGC 2859

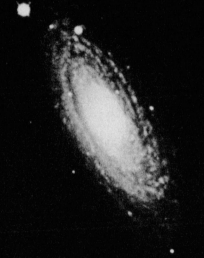

Sb NGC 2841

SBb NGC 5850

Sc NGC 5457(M101)

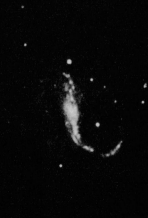

SBc NGC 7479

STARS IN THE GALAXIES

THE BLUE GIANT STARS of the spiral arms appear to be spendthrift consumers of their hydrogen supply. It has been calculated that they can continue at their presently-observed rate of energy production for only about 100 million years. We would therefore expect to find them only in Population I sections of the galaxies, among "new" stars. In the older parts, where no interstellar gas remains, we would not expect to find them. There are some red stars in such regions, but they are smaller and dimmer.

The brightest stars in the elliptical galaxies, in the central portions of the spirals, and in the globular clusters of our own system are red giants, considerably brighter than the red stars of the spiral arms. These are the older Population II stars which were probably formed early in the life history of galaxies.

Of course, there are other stars in both of these type-regions. Stars like our own yellowish sun are not at all uncommon in the sections of the Milky Way that are comparable in many respects to the spiral arms of other galaxies. We must remember that only the extremely brilliant stars can be clearly identified in the distant galaxies. Ordinary ones, like those in our vicinity, cannot be photographed individually.

As mentioned earlier, the appearance of cepheid variables in the galaxies has permitted our most dependable method of determining their distances. Novae and supernovae have been found, too, as have many other types of variable stars well known in our galaxy. There is reason to believe that the fainter stars, like those so familiar to us in our earth's night sky, also exist in other parts of the universe.

Spiral nebula in Virgo seen edge on
Photo: courtesy Mt. Wilson and Palomar Observatories; 200-inch photograph

THE AGE OF THE UNIVERSE

ONE OF THE MOST ACTIVE controversies in modern astronomy has to do with the age of the universe. Most astronomers believe that some catastrophic event in the past touched off the beginnings of the galactic systems as they are known today. A few support the view that we live in a universe in which there is constant creation of new matter which, in turn, feeds the birth of new stars and galaxies.

The problem of the age of the universe does not exist if one accepts the theory of continuous creation, for if this theory is correct, the universe has some new parts and some old parts. Furthermore, it was always so, and always will be. If, on the other hand, we accept the notion of the explosion of a primordial atom long ago, the age of the universe as we know it must date from that event.

One way to estimate age is to study the make-up of stars. We are quite certain that they obtain their energy—most of them, at least—by converting hydrogen to helium. We can estimate how long a star has been radiating at the present rate, and how long it may continue to radiate in a similar fashion. But there is no assurance that the energy process remains constant; on the contrary, we believe that stars do change. The best evidence leads us to the figure of some four to five billion years for the age of stars in our galaxy and in globular clusters.

Another evidence of the age of the universe comes from the theory of the expanding universe. (See next page.) This gives us a much broader base than using a star or group of stars. If galaxies actually do move away from each other at a rate than can be calculated, then it should be possible to determine mathematically the time when they were all at the same place; this must have been the time of the great explosion. It is not easy to make such calculations, for numerous corrections must be made, and there must be many assumptions involved, as there are for individual stars. It has been done, however, and the result is of the same order as for the other method: 4½ billion years. At least, this figure is the best guess we can make.

NGC 1300 barred spiral nebula in Eridanus
Photo: courtesy Mt. Wilson and Palomar Observatories; 200-inch photograph

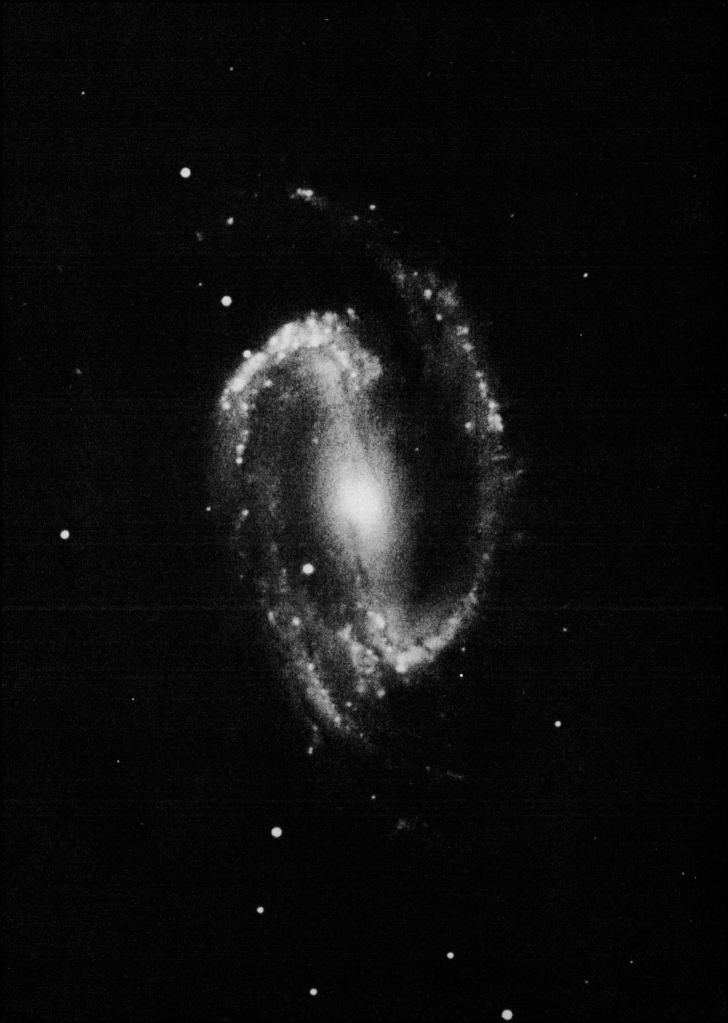

THE EXPANDING UNIVERSE

In 1929, Edwin P. Hubble announced that all of the distant galaxies seemed to be receding from the Milky Way with a velocity that increases with distance. This discovery posed some difficult problems, for any theory about the origin and nature of the universe had to explain why and how such a condition could exist.

The evidence for the expansion of the universe is good. It is based on the "red shift" observed in the spectra of most exterior galaxies. It has long been known that the lines of a dark-line spectrum would shift toward the red or long wave-length end of the color band when an object was moving away from us, and toward the blue or short-wave-length end when the object was approaching. The principle had been used successfully to determine the manner in which Saturn's rings revolve, the rotation of some planets, and the motions of stars. When the spectroscope is directed toward the galaxies, there is usually a shift toward the red, and the shift is greater for the distant systems.

It is possible that there is an as yet unknown principle in physics, other than the velocity effect, which could account for the red shift. One theory is that the light from the galaxies is required to penetrate such huge distances to reach us that it simply is "tired" or "fatigued." Gas or dust between the galaxies reddens the light in the same way that dust clouds sometimes color the sun, but this well-known effect does not explain the observed shift of dark spectral lines from their normal position. The most reasonable conclusion is that the galaxies actually are moving away from us (and from each other) and that the universe is expanding.

Does this mean that the galactic population in telescope range is decreasing, that galaxies are moving out of the field of view? If we accept the theory of expansion, that is certainly a possibility. Perhaps at some date in the distant future, the Milky Way will be more isolated in space than it is now.

Cluster of galaxies in Corona Borealis; distance about 210 million light years
Photo: courtesy Mt. Wilson and Palomar Observatories; 200-inch photograph

FROM HERE TO INFINITY

BEFORE GALILEO looked into the skies with his telescope, few men had questioned the earth's position as the greatest, most important object in existence. Yet once other planets were recognized, and the earth was viewed correctly as just one among several worlds attending the sun in its journey through space, it became clear that the attitude of man about his universe had to change. Infinity reached out beyond our neighbor worlds.

The next step was taken when the true character of the sun became known. As one among many stars, it lost its uniqueness. If, as the evidence indicated, the other stars were as large or larger, though they presented to us but a point-source of brightness, then the estimates of distances from one to the other had to be enlarged greatly from earlier concepts. Infinity had to be pushed out far enough to explain how this could be.

Then came the telescopes of the modern era, with their ability to probe the extremes of our Milky Way. The "city of stars," of which the sun is a member, was defined and measured not in millions of miles, but in light-years. However, that was not the end; more lay beyond, and infinity was stretched again to meet the new facts.

The gigantic new telescopes and their newfound ally, radio telescopes, continue to press ever outward in the search for greater knowledge. Whenever new devices have been built which are capable of seeing more or farther, there has been more to see. There is nothing to indicate that the end is in sight.

Infinity, that ultimate point beyond all else, is just as elusive now as it was hundreds of years ago. But, there is a difference; much of the interval between here and infinity has been explored and charted.

Field and faint galaxies in Coma Berenices; some of the faintest nebulae are indicated; distances from 500 to 1,000 million light-years
Photo: courtesy Mt. Wilson and Palomar Observatories; 200-inch photograph

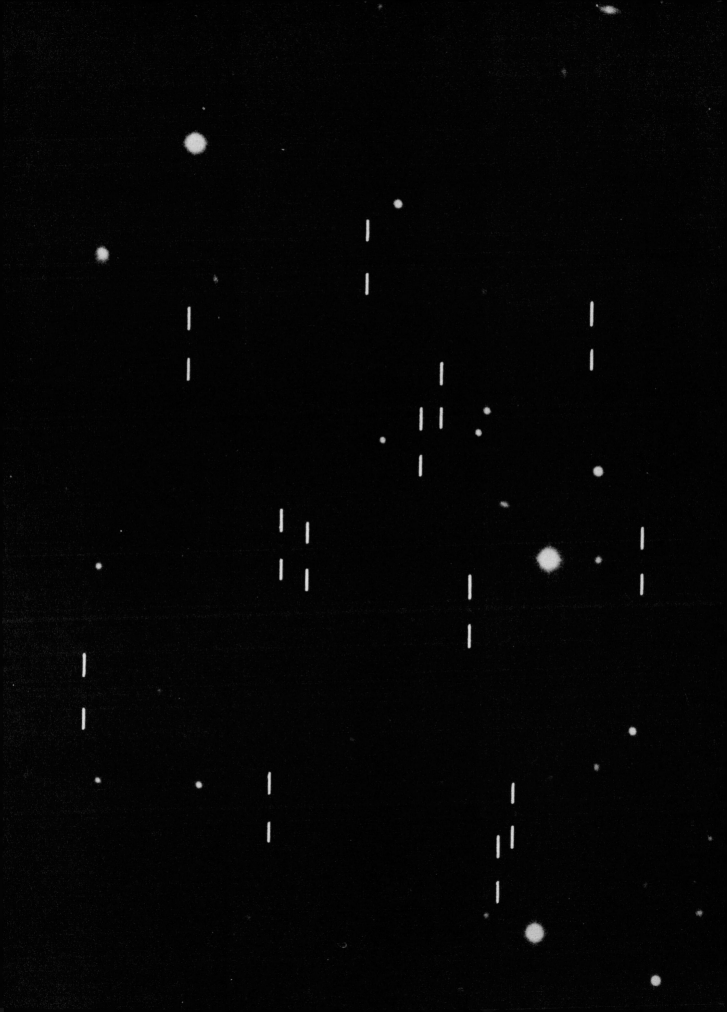

CHAPTER VIII

THE STARS AROUND THE YEAR

DURING THE YEAR, the revolution of the earth around the sun faces us in many directions in space, allowing us to scan completely the stars beyond the solar system in most directions. Each day, as the earth rotates, our view also sweeps around the sky, but for the part of the rotation that takes place during daylight when we face toward the sun, stars are hidden in the brightness of the day.

Thus we have a composite, changing picture of the entire sky from night to night through the year. The stars we see are often referred to as stars of the seasons, depending upon when they are seen in the heavens. The stars of spring are those that appear in the eastern part of the sky as night comes on in the springtime. Three months later, however, the revolution of the earth has taken us around the sun a quarter of the way, so that we face toward a different direction in space in the after-sunset sky of summer. At that time, the stars we see in the east are known as the summer stars. Similarly, we identify the stars of the autumn and winter.

SPRING STARS

THE BIG DIPPER is the most conspicuous group of stars in the evening skies of springtime. It has been identified since mythological times as an unusual arrangement of stars, sometimes called a plow, a royal chariot, or a carriage pulled by three horses. The seven bright stars of the dipper are not a complete constellation; Ursa Major (the Great Bear) includes the stars of the dipper and many others in the same region. The bowl of the dipper is part of the bear's back and the handle is supposed to be his tail.

The two stars at the end of the bowl, Merak and Dubhe, point to the pole star. Extend an imaginary line from Merak through Dubhe away from the bowl, and the first bright star along that line is Polaris, the North Star. The point on the horizon just below Polaris is labeled north.

By extending a curved line through the three stars of the dipper's handle and down the sky, two other bright spring stars can be recognized. The first along the line is Arcturus, in Boötes, and the bright star further down is Spica, in Virgo.

Directly under the bowl of the Big Dipper, opposite the direction of the North Star, the constellation Leo the Lion can be found. The easiest way to recognize the lion is to look for the Sickle, a group of stars very much like a backwards question mark. The round part of the question mark outlines the lion's head and mane. The dot of the question mark is the bright star Regulus, at the lion's heart. To the left of the question mark, three other stars form a triangle to mark the hind quarters of Leo. Denebola, at the tip of the triangle, is the tip of the lion's tail.

Regulus and Spica can sometimes be identified by the moon. Both of these very bright stars lie very nearly along the path in which the moon travels around the earth. On spring evenings, near the times of full moon, it will pass close to these stars and may even pass in front of them, an event known as an occultation.

SUMMER STARS

By the end of June, the stars of spring are low in the west in early evening, and the eastern skies contain the stars of the summer, illustrated here. This part of the heavens is dominated by a group of three very bright stars, known collectively as the Great Summer Triangle. Later in the summer months, the triangle will appear higher and further west as darkness draws on.

The three bright stars in the triangle are Altair, Deneb, and Vega, often remembered because their initials form the abbreviation of the very common word advertisement (adv). Each of the stars belongs to a different constellation, Altair to Aquila, the Eagle; Deneb to Cygnus, the Swan; and Vega to Lyra, the Lyre.

Altair has two fainter stars on either side of it, and the three form a nearly straight line with Altair in the middle. Alshain is the star above, and Tarazed is the star below Altair in the threesome. Deneb is at the top of a group of stars known as Cygnus, the Swan or the Northern Cross. This cross is much larger than the famous Southern Cross. From Deneb, the long arm of the cross points into the center of the Summer Triangle. The third star, Vega, can sometimes be identified by the row of faint stars on each side forming the outline of the musical instrument, the Lyre, which gives the constellation its name. Vega is brighter than either Altair or Deneb, and can be readily distinguished from the other two by its brightness.

Low in the southern skies during summer evenings, there is a bright reddish star known as Antares. The stars around it form the outline of Scorpius, the Scorpion. Antares is at the heart of the Scorpion, its head and "feelers" extend westward in front (to the right on the map), and the long curved tail extends to the east, with Shaula marking the tip of the tail. Just behind the tail of the Scorpion is the constellation Sagittarius, the Archer. The stars in the Archer can best be recognized, however, by the arrangement that resembles a teapot, shown in the lower left corner.

On clear, dark nights of the summer, the glow of light from the Milky Way extends from the Northern Cross into the south towards the tail of the Scorpion.

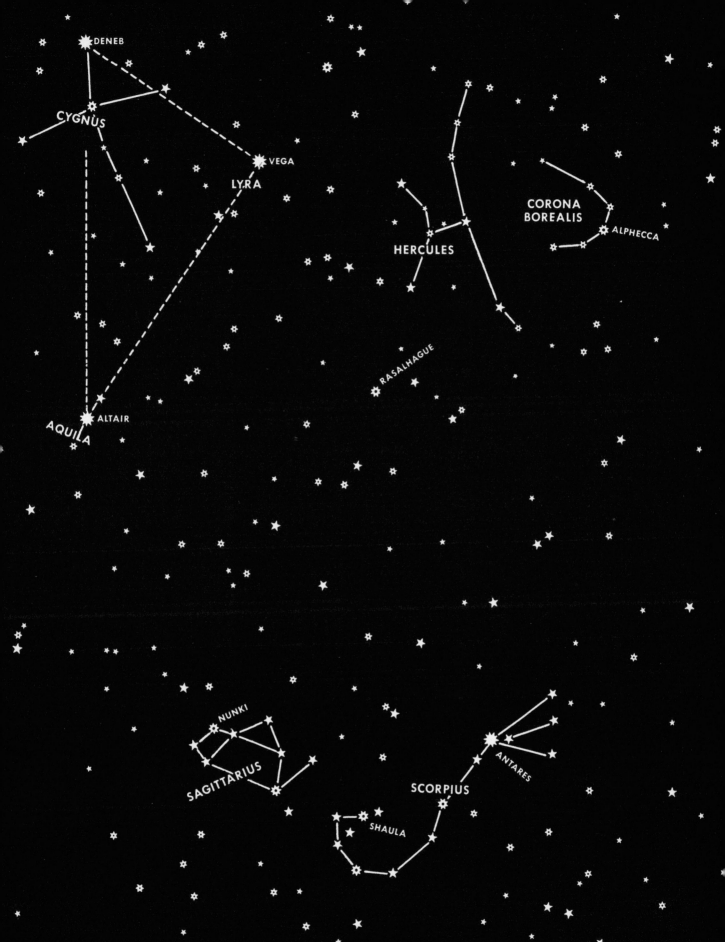

AUTUMN STARS

THE SUMMER TRIANGLE and other stars of the summer sky appear in the west a few hours after sunset in the middle of autumn, and the eastern sky contains the stars shown here. Among these stars, the Square of Pegasus is probably the most obvious arrangement with which to begin.

Four bright stars appear as a huge box, or square. They are named from the constellation Pegasus, the Flying Horse, which contains some of them and many other nearby stars. Algenib, Markab, and Scheat form one of the wings of the horse. His neck and head stretch westward toward the star Enif. It is difficult to trace Pegasus because only the forequarters of the horse are represented in the figure, and it is arranged upside down in the heavens. Early at night in October, the Square is high up in the southeast.

Extending north and east from the star Alpheratz, there can be seen a line of three bright stars, including Alpheratz. They trace the constellation Andromeda, the chained maiden, in that direction. Further along the line, a fourth star may also be seen—Mirfak, in the constellation Perseus, the Champion.

Two bright stars of the southern sky can be located from the sides of the Square of Pegasus. Follow a line down through Alpheratz and Algenib to the bright star Diphda, in the constellation Cetus, the Whale. A line down through the western (right hand) stars of the square, Scheat and Markab, points toward Fomalhaut, in the Southern Fish, Piscis Australis.

The sun is in this part of the sky in the spring. On March 20 or 21, the first day of spring, the sun is at the vernal equinox. This point in the skies is located just below Algenib, about the same distance below as the distance between Alpheratz and Algenib, and a little to the west, in the stars of the constellation Pisces. A few thousand years ago, the sun was in the constellation Aries on the first day of spring, near the star Hamal shown on this map. For that reason, the vernal equinox is often called the First Point of Aries, although it is not in Aries at the present time.

DENEB

ALMACH

ANDROMEDA

MIRACH

ALPHERATZ   SCHEAT

PEGASUS

ALGENIB   MARKAB

ENIF

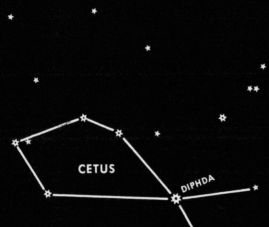

CETUS   DIPHDA

FOMALHAUT

ACHERNAR

WINTER STARS

THE CONSTELLATION ORION, centrally located on this map, appears as the most dominant and most easily recognized group of stars in the sky. It provides an excellent guide to the others in this region of the heavens.

Orion is known as the Hunter or the Giant. His figure is outlined by the brilliant stars Betelgeuse and Rigel and their fainter neighbors Bellatrix and Saiph. In the center of the box-like arrangement formed by these four, there are three conspicuous stars of nearly equal brightness. They form the line of Orion's Belt. Another line of still fainter stars curves down from the Belt to become the Sword of Orion.

Imagine a line in the sky in both directions from the three belt stars. The reddish-yellow star directly above the belt is Betelgeuse, a huge red giant hundreds of times larger than the sun, and also a variable star. Near Betelgeuse, to the right, is Bellatrix, both stars supposedly locating the tips of Orion's shoulders. Below the belt, the brightest star is Rigel, a tremendously luminous blue giant, thousands of times more brilliant than the sun. To the left of Rigel, the star completing the outline of Orion's figure is Saiph.

Following along the line of the belt to the right, there is another bright red star, Aldebaran, part of a V-shaped group in the constellation Taurus, the Bull. The stars of the V are supposed to represent the Bull's nose. These stars, except for Aldebaran, which just happens to be in the same direction from the earth, belong to the galactic star cluster known as the Hyades. Further to the west, to the right in the map, there is another cluster, the Pleiades.

Following to the left with the line of Orion's Belt, we come to the brightest star that can be seen from any part of the earth at any time of the year. It is Sirius, in Canis Major, the Great Dog. An outline of the dog can be imagined by considering Sirius to be at the tip of his nose and locating his other features from the more prominent stars nearby. Canopus, shown in the lower part of the map, is the second brightest star we see, but it is below the southern horizon, or quite close to it, from most parts of the United States.

The remaining bright stars of the winter sky, Capella, Procyon, Pollux and Castor, and others shown on the map can also be located by reference to Orion or to the groups identified from Orion.

MIRFAK

MENKALINAN   CAPELLA

CASTOR

POLLUX

AURIGA

PLEIADES

GEMINI

ELNATH

TAURUS

ALDEBARAN

BETELGEUSE

PROCYON

BELLATRIX

ORION

SAIPH

RIGEL

SIRIUS

CANIS
MAJOR

CANOPUS

STARS AROUND THE POLE

THIS IS A SUMMER MAP of the northern stars, with the upper part of the map highest in the sky. On autumn nights, the stars on the right side of the map are highest in the early evening, and the map should be turned so that the Big Dipper is lowest on the page. In winter, the bottom of the map is uppermost in the sky, and the map should be turned upside down to conform to the arrangement seen during the hours after sunset. In the spring, the Big Dipper is highest in the early evening, and the map should be turned to bring it uppermost. Every clear night of the year, however, all the stars around the pole can be seen, drifting slowly in a counterclockwise fashion reflecting the rotation of the earth beneath them.

Note that the North Star, at the center of the page, is located at the end of the handle in the Little Dipper. This group of stars is difficult to see because its stars, except for Polaris, in the handle, and Kochab, in the bowl, are quite faint. One easy way to find its position is to note how it is related to the Big Dipper. The bowls of the two dippers open toward one another. Though either one may be uppermost, depending on the time of the night and year, the bowl of one will always seem to be "pouring" into the other. Kochab and its brightest neighbor, at the end of the Little Dipper's bowl, wheel around the pole quite close to Polaris. They are often called the Guardians of the Pole for this reason.

Most of the other stars in this circumpolar region are not very bright, except for those in Cassiopeia, on the opposite side of the pole star from the Big Dipper. The five brightest stars in Cassiopeia are arranged something like a flattened letter W, or an M, depending on how they are observed. They are supposed to represent a queen on her throne.

The other groups in the map are more difficult to find. With a little practice they can be traced as shown in the outlines of the chart. These stars can also be related to the seasonal maps of the skies by matching the brighter stars shown at the borders of the circumpolar region.

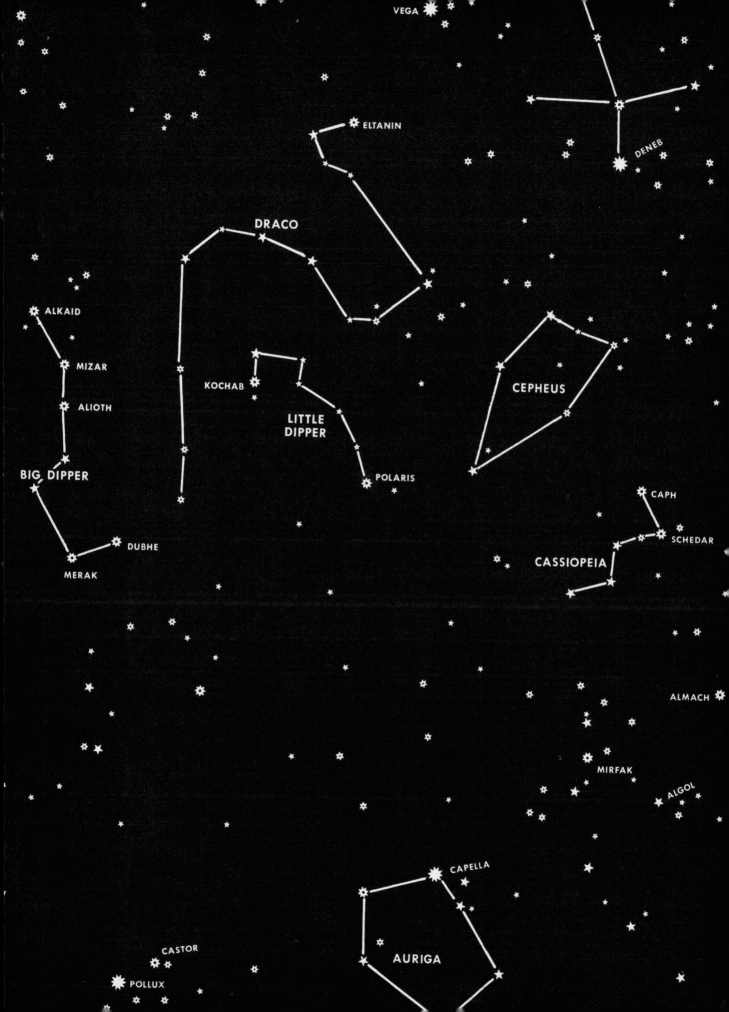

INDEX

Index

Numbers in **boldface** show full treatment of subject.